SHACK-HARTMANN AND INTERFEROMETRIC
HYBRID WAVEFRONT SENSOR

DISSERTATION

Troy R. Ellis, Captain, USAF

AFIT/DEO/ENG/11-01

DEPARTMENT OF THE AIR FORCE
AIR UNIVERSITY

AIR FORCE INSTITUTE OF TECHNOLOGY

Wright-Patterson Air Force Base, Ohio

Shack-Hartmann and Interferometric Hybrid Wavefront Sensor

Troy R. Ellis

AFIT/DEO/ENG/11-01

SHACK-HARTMANN AND INTERFEROMETRIC
HYBRID WAVEFRONT SENSOR

DISSERTATION

Presented to the Faculty

Graduate School of Engineering and Management

Air Force Institute of Technology

Air University

Air Education and Training Command

In Partial Fulfillment of the Requirements for the

Degree of Doctor of Philosophy

Troy R. Ellis, BS,MS

Captain, USAF

March 2011

AFIT/DEO/ENG/11-01

SHACK-HARTMANN AND INTERFEROMETRIC
HYBRID WAVEFRONT SENSOR

Troy R. Ellis, BS,MS
Captain, USAF

Approved:

Maj Jason D. Schmidt, PhD (Chairman)	13 Feb 11 Date
Stephen C. Cain, PhD (Member)	22 Feb 2011 Date
Matthew Fickus, PhD (Member)	18 Feb 11 Date

Accepted:

M.U. Thomas, PhD
Dean, Graduate School of
Engineering and Management

14 Mar 11
Date

Abstract

Wavefront sensors (WFS) use intensity measurements to estimate the phase of an incident optical field for applications such as high-quality surface measurements and atmospheric compensation with adaptive optics (AO). Shack-Hartmann (SH) WFS's use intensity measurements at the focal plane to estimate local wavefront tilts, which can be reconstructed into wavefront estimates. Self-referencing-interferometer (SRI) WFS's use pupil-plane interferogram-intensity measurements to estimate the phase of the incident optical field.

The SRI and SH WFS's have strengths and weaknesses that turn out to complement each other quite well over a range of operating conditions. Specifically, the difference between the mathematical formulation of SRI measurements and the actual phase at DM actuators has been shown to be insensitive to scintillation. In contrast, the SH WFS's formulation error can be significant in strong scintillation. Conversely, the SH WFS has actually shown better performance than the SRI in cases of low scintillation strength and large subapertures relative to atmospheric coherence width. Together, the SRI and the SH WFS provide better performance over a wider range of atmospheric conditions than either WFS could do on its own.

This document reports results of wave-optics simulations used to test the performance of a hybrid WFS designed to combine the SRI and SH WFS's in an optimal way. Optimal hybrid-WFS design required a thorough analysis of the noise characteristics of each WFS to produce noise models that assist in the design of an optimal phase-estimation algorithm. Feasible architectures and algorithms for combining WFS's were chosen, and the noise models of the individual WFS's were combined to form a model for the noise-induced error of the resulting hybrid WFS. The hybrid WFS and phase-estimation algorithm developed through this work showed improvement over a comparable stand-alone SRI in open-loop wave-optics simulations.

Acknowledgements

I would like to express my sincere gratitude to my advisor, Maj. Jason Schmidt, whose patience and guidance have allowed me to get to this point in my research. He is one of the best teachers I have had, and his editing and advice have made this and all other reports related to my PhD research immensely better products. I would also like to thank my son, who I credit with motivating me to embark on such a difficult endeavor. Without the encouragement I gained by seeing the spark of pride in his eyes when I told him about this opportunity, I would have probably let it pass by. Therefore, this work and this dissertation are dedicated to him. Thanks, buddy.

Troy R. Ellis

Table of Contents

Page

Abstract   iv

Acknowledgements   v

List of Figures   ix

List of Symbols   xii

List of Abbreviations   xiv

I.   Introduction   1
         1.1   Problem Definition   2
         1.2   Proposed Solution and Approach   5
         1.3   Goals of Proposed Research   6

II.   Background   7
         2.1   Wave Optics   7
               2.1.1   The Wave-Particle Duality of Light   7
               2.1.2   Light as an Electromagnetic Wave   8
               2.1.3   Wave Equations for Optics   9
               2.1.4   The Angular Spectrum   12
               2.1.5   Optical Elements and Aberrations   14
               2.1.6   Numerical Propagation and Sampling   16
               2.1.7   Validity of Wave Optics Simulations   18
         2.2   Optical Coherence   21
         2.3   Photodetection Statistics   24
         2.4   Atmospheric Turbulence   27
               2.4.1   The Optical Structure of the Atmosphere   27
               2.4.2   Optical Turbulence Statistics   31
         2.5   The Shack-Hartmann Wavefront Sensor   35
               2.5.1   Theory   36
               2.5.2   Measuring Spot Displacement   38
               2.5.3   Dynamic Range   40
               2.5.4   Noise-Induced Centroid Error   43
               2.5.5   Impact of Irradiance Fluctuations   44
         2.6   The Self-Referencing Interferometer   45
               2.6.1   Theory of Interference   45

	2.6.2	Fringe Visibility and Coherence	47
	2.6.3	Phase-Shifting Interferometry	48
	2.6.4	Self Referencing Interferometer	50
2.7	Estimation Theory		54
	2.7.1	The Decision-Making Process	56
	2.7.2	Likelihood Functions	57
	2.7.3	Cost and Risk Functions	57
	2.7.4	Bias, Variance, and Mean Square Error	58
	2.7.5	Maximum-Likelihood Estimation	60
2.8	Phase Unwrapping and Reconstruction		62
	2.8.1	Phase Unwrapping	63
	2.8.2	Phase Reconstruction from Slope Measurements	68

III.	Review of Related Research		75
	3.1	Extended Beacons	75
	3.2	Wavefront Sensors in Strong Scintillation	76
	3.3	Self-Referencing Interferometer	78
	3.4	Shack-Hartmann Wavefront Sensor	79
	3.5	Work Combining WFS's for Deep Turbulence	81
	3.6	Motivation for a Hybrid WFS	83

IV.	A Model for Shot-Noise-Induced Centroid Error		85
	4.1	Introduction	85
	4.2	Centroid-Error Variance in Scintillation	90
		4.2.1	Impact of the Intensity Probability Density . . .	96
		4.2.2	Accounting for Atmospheric Spread in SH Spots	99
	4.3	Testing the Model against Wave-Optics Simulations . . .	103
		4.3.1	Wave-Optics Atmospheric Propagations	103
		4.3.2	Shack-Hartmann Model	108
		4.3.3	Centroid-Error Variance Model	109
		4.3.4	Simulation Results	109
	4.4	Conclusion	112

V.	A Model for Shot-Noise-Induced Phase Error in SRI Measurements		115
	5.1	Introduction	115
	5.2	Derivation of SRI Photon-Noise-Induced Phase Error . .	116
	5.3	Monte Carlo Simulations	126
	5.4	Testing the Model against Wave-Optics Simulations . . .	134
	5.5	Conclusion	137

VI.   Hybrid Wavefront Sensor   138
       6.1   Introduction   138
       6.2   SRI Phase Variance Model   140
       6.3   Shack-Hartmann Phase Variance Model   141
       6.4   Hybrid WFS Architecture   143
       6.5   Maximum-Likelihood, Weighted-Average Hybrid WFS .   148
       6.6   Wave-Optics Tests of Hybrid-WFS Performance   155
             6.6.1   Atmospheric Fields   156
             6.6.2   Simulation Results   156
       6.7   Conclusion   163

VII.   Conclusion   165
       7.1   Model of SH-WFS Centroid Error   165
       7.2   Model of SRI Phase Error   166
       7.3   Hybrid WFS   166
       7.4   Research Challenges   167
       7.5   Future Work   168

Bibliography   170

List of Figures

Figure   Page

1   AO system with a hybrid wavefront sensor   2

2   Vacuum-propagated point source   20

3   Tilt sensor   37

4   Quad-cell detector   39

5   Truncation error of centroid.   43

6   Fringe visibility and energy imbalance   49

7   Point-diffraction interferometer.   50

8   Self-Referencing Interferometer.   52

9   Decision-making process for an imaging system   55

10   Wrapped and unwrapped phase   63

11   Example of phase near a branch point   66

12   Branch cuts in atmosperic phase   69

13   Fried's alignment geometry.   70

14   Hudgin's alignment geometry.   71

15   Southwell's alignment geometry.   72

16   Overlaid Hudgin and Southwell geometries.   73

17   Shack-Hartmann Subaperture Geometry   87

18   Centroid Error Vs. Pixel Size   96

19   Impact of Intensity pdf on Centroid-Error Model   98

20   Shack-Hartmann Subaperture Average Spot Shape, $d/r_0 = 1/4$ 100

21   Shack-Hartmann Subaperture Average Spot Shape, $d/r_0 = 1/2$ 101

22   Shack-Hartmann Subaperture Average Spot Shape, $d/r_0 = 1$.   102

23   Aperture Size in Wave-Optics Simulations   104

24   Uninterpolated Data Intensity and Phase Statistics, $d/r_0 = 1$.   105

25   Uninterpolated Data Intensity and Phase Statistics, $d/r_0 = 1/4$ 106

Figure		Page
26	Interpolated Data Intensity and Phase Statistics, $d/r_0 = 1/4$.	107
27	Centroid-error Vs. photon level, no scintillation	110
28	Centroid-error simulation results for $d/r_0 = 1$	111
29	Centroid-error simulation results for $d/r_0 = 1/2$	112
30	Centroid-error simulation results for $d/r_0 = 1/4$	113
31	Full centroid-error simulation results	114
32	Four-bin phase-shifting SRI	117
33	Example of SRI interferograms	119
34	SRI measurements on the complex plain	121
35	SRI Monte Carlo photocount variance, 16^2 subapertures	127
36	SRI Monte Carlo photocount variance, 32^2 subapertures	128
37	SRI sampling error (Monte Carlo), 50 phot./subap.	130
38	SRI sampling error (Monte Carlo), 200 phot./subap.	131
39	SRI phase-error variance (Monte Carlo), 50 photons, $d = D/16$	132
40	SRI phase-error variance (Monte Carlo), 200 photons, $d = D/16$	133
41	SRI phase-error variance (Monte Carlo), 50 photons, $d = D/32$	133
42	SRI phase-error variance (Monte Carlo), 200 photons, $d = D/32$	134
43	SRI phase-error variance (wave-optics), $d = D/16$, $d/r_0 = 1$ . .	135
44	SRI phase-error variance (wave-optics), 50 photons, $d = D/16$.	135
45	SRI phase-error variance (wave-optics), 200 photons, $d = D/16$	136
46	SRI and SH phase variances from models	145
47	SH slope-reconstruction geometries	147
48	Hybrid-WFS alignment geometry	148
49	Weighting of SRI estimate	153
50	Choosing optimum splitting parameter γ	155
51	Hybrid wave-optics LSPES Vs. Rytov number	158
52	Hybrid's LSPES improvement over SRI	158
53	Stability of hybrid's LSPES	160

Figure   Page

54   Hybrid's performance compared to SRI & SH WFS's   161

55   Hybrid's DMPFS Vs. Rytov number   162

56   Ensembles of hybrid's DMPFS   163

List of Symbols

Symbol   Page

c Velocity of Light   8

ϵ_0 Permittivity of Free Space   8

μ_0 Permeability of Free Space   8

$\boldsymbol{E}$ Electric Field Intensity   9

$\boldsymbol{D}$ Electric Flux Density   9

$\boldsymbol{H}$ Magnetic Field Intensity   9

$\boldsymbol{B}$ Magnetic Flux Density   9

$\boldsymbol{J}$ Current Density   9

ρ_v Charge Density   10

n Refractive Index   11

$U(\boldsymbol{r}, t)$ Optical Field   11

λ Optical Wavelength   12

k Optical Wave Number   12

$A(f_X, f_Y)$ Angular Spectrum   13

$\mathcal{P}(x, y)$ Generalized Pupil Function   14

$\Gamma_{12}(\tau)$ Mutual Coherence Function   22

$|\gamma_{12}(\tau)|$ Degree of Coherence   22

$|\mu_{12}|$ Coherence Factor   22

J_{12} Mutual Intensity   24

μ_{12} Complex Coherence Factor   24

K Number of Photoevents   24

$D_\psi(r)$ Wave Structure Function   27

σ_χ^2 Log-Amplitude Variance (Rytov Number)   27

θ_0 Isoplanatic Angle   27

L_0 Outer Scale   28

Symbol		Page
l_0	Inner Scale	28
$D_n(r)$	Refractive-Index Structure Function	29
ρ_0	Spatial Coherence Radius	33
r_0	Atmospheric Coherence Width (Fried's Parameter)	33
$\tilde{\sigma}_I^2$	Scintillation Index	34
σ_I^2	Intensity (or Irradiance) Variance	35
$\langle I \rangle$	Mean Intensity (or Irradiance)	35
$\sigma_{\ln I}^2$	Log-Intensity (or Irradiance) Variance (Rytov Variance) .	35
d	Subaperture Side Length	37
$\mathcal{V}$	Fringe Visibility	47
$\Re(u)$	Real Part of Complex u	66
$\Im(u)$	Imaginary Part of Complex u	66
σ_{sri}^2	SRI's Phase-Error Variance	140
σ_{sh}^2	SH WFS's Phase-Error Variance	141
$\sigma_{\hat{\phi}}^2$	Hybrid WFS's Phase-Error Variance	150

List of Abbreviations

Abbreviation		Page
AO	Adaptive Optics	1
FSM	Fast Steering Mirror	1
DM	Deformable Mirror	1
WFS	Wavefront Sensor	1
SH	Shack-Hartmann	1
SRI	Self-Referencing Interferometer	1
ABL	Airborne Laser	3
HEL	High-Energy Laser	3
EM	Electro-Magnetic	7
OPD	Optical Pathlength Difference	15
MCF	Mutual Coherence Function	22
PSD	Power Spectral Density	23
MTF	Modulation Transfer Function	33
CRLB	Cramer-Rao Lower Bound	41
PDI	Point-Diffraction Interferometer	45
SMF	Single-Mode Fiber	52
pdf	Probability Density Function	57
MSE	Mean Square Error	59
MLE	Maximum-Likelihood Estimate	60
CRLB	Cramer-Rao Lower Bound	61
LSI	Lateral-Shearing Interferometer	77
AFRL	Air Force Research Laboratory	78
SOR	Starfire Optical Range	78
LADAR	Laser Detection and Ranging	81
SPGD	Stochastic Parallel Gradient Descent	81

Abbreviation		Page
WBSPGD	Wavefront-Based Stochastic Parallel Gradient Descent . .	81
PSF	Point-Spread Function	89
FWHM	Full Width at Half Max	95
OTF	Optical Transfer Function	99
SNR	Signal-to-Noise Ratio	124
PES	Phase-Estimation Strehl Ratio	155
DMPFS	DM Phase-Fitting Strehl Ratio	156
LSPES	Least-Squares-Phase-Estimation Strehl Ratio	157

SHACK-HARTMANN AND INTERFEROMETRIC
HYBRID WAVEFRONT SENSOR

I. Introduction

Adaptive optics (AO) systems correct wavefront distortions caused by propagation through turbulent media. Figure 1 shows a diagram of an AO system designed to correct optical distortions caused by propagation of light through the earth's atmosphere. In this system, a beacon provides a reference wavefront that is corrupted by atmospheric turbulence before entering the AO system where optics collimate the light from the incoming beacon and a tilt sensor combined with a fast steering mirror (FSM) work together to track the beacon and keep it centered in the system field of view. After the FSM, the incoming light encounters the deformable mirror (DM), which works to correct the wavefront distortions caused by propagation through the atmospheric turbulence. A hybrid wavefront sensor (WFS) combines measurements from two different WFS's into estimates of the wavefront distortions, and a computerized control system then uses the wavefront measurements to command actuators on the DM, improving the performance of the primary optical system. Two WFS's used for AO are the Shack-Hartmann (SH) WFS and the self-referencing interferometer (SRI). Shack-Hartmann WFS's use intensity measurements at the focal plane to estimate local wavefront tilts, which can be reconstructed into wavefront estimates. Self-referencing interferometers use pupil-plane interferogram-intensity measurements to estimate the real and imaginary parts of the incident optical field, which then provide a means of estimating the optical phase. The SRI and SH WFS's have strengths and weaknesses that turn out to complement each other quite well over a range of operating conditions. This dissertation presents a hybrid WFS optimally designed to handle noise-induced phase-errors. In open-loop computer simulations, the proposed hybrid WFS performs better than a comparable stand-alone SRI.

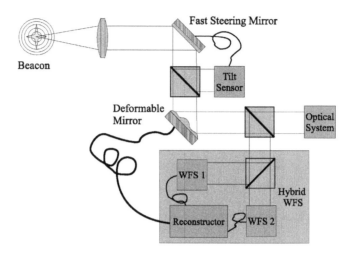

Figure 1:   AO system with a hybrid wavefront sensor

The remainder of this introductory chapter defines the problem, describes the solution, and states the goals of the research. The dissertation is organized into seven chapters. Background information necessary for understanding the problem and solution are presented in Ch. II, and the review of related research is presented in Ch. III. In Ch. IV, a model is presented that predicts centroid error resulting from atmospherically induced fluctuating intensity coupled with photon noise in a Shack-Hartmann WFS. Chapter V presents a model for photon-noise-induced phase error in the SRI, which shows that SRI measurements actually do depend on scintillation strength. In Ch. VI, the two noise models are used to develop a maximum-likelihood, weighted-average approach to combining the SH and SRI WFS's that shows improved performance relative to a stand-alone SRI in open-loop computer simulations. Finally, Ch. VII summarizes conclusions of this dissertation, discusses challenges encountered during the course of this research, and suggests areas for future work.

1.1   Problem Definition

Historically, the choice of WFS has been heavily influenced by the intended application's operating conditions. For example, the bulk of the atmosphere is concentrated at low altitude in a relatively thin layer, so refractive index fluctuations due to atmospheric turbulence have the greatest impact on light propagating through the first few kilometers above sea level. Also, atmospheric refractive index fluctuations are relatively weak and do not cause extreme wavefront distortions unless the waves experience thick layers of strong turbulence or have long propagation paths over which to accumulate large phase deviations. Therefore, astronomical telescopes are often located at high altitudes (in a thin atmosphere) and look more or less straight up to avoid thick layers of atmospheric turbulence located far from the imaging system's light-collecting aperture. In favorable conditions, scintillation, which is the occurrence of random amplitude fluctuations in the received optical field, can be neglected without significant performance implications. Also, astronomical AO systems often use spatially incoherent beacons with limited photon flux (natural stars in the early days of AO) and therefore favor a WFS that can operate with low levels of incoherent light. The Shack-Hartmann WFS, which provides consistent, reliable performance in weak scintillation with dim beacons, accordingly became the most reasonable choice of WFS for astronomical AO. However, as AO systems were pushed to deal with a broader range of operating conditions, limitations of the SH WFS became evident, especially for light propagating over long propagation paths through constant-strength turbulence.

Turbulence associated with long, horizontal propagation paths causes scintillation, which in turn causes problems for the SH WFS and can severely limit the effectiveness of applications such as the Airborne Laser (ABL) [5]. The ABL flies at high altitude searching for recently launched missiles to then track and shoot down with its onboard high-energy laser (HEL). The ABL and other applications, such as astronomical AO with a laser guide star, use an artificial beacon with quasi-monochromatic light, which suggests the possibility that coherent WFS's might be effective. The SH WFS's poor performance in strong turbulence and the availability of a powerful, narrow-band beacon motivated the development of the SRI. The SRI is a relatively new approach to wavefront sensing that promises to extend AO operating regimes beyond weak fluctuations of the propagation medium and possibly provide drastic performance improvement in optical systems operating over long, horizontal propagation paths. However, it is unrealistic to expect that the SRI can replace the SH WFS in all AO applications. For example, applications that experience broadband, extended, and dim beacons are much better served by the SH WFS. While lasers can provide narrow-band, high-energy beacons, these beacons can still become extended.

The technical problems addressed by this research are interrelated, and several are identified here. The primary problem motivating this research is the need for a wavefront sensor that can operate over a wider range of scintillation strengths, like the SRI can do, and still be able to perform with broadband, extended, and potentially dim beacons, which the SH WFS can do. The specific solution presented by this research is that of optimally combining a SH WFS with an SRI and evaluating the resulting hybrid WFS's performance over a range of scintillation strengths, atmospheric conditions, and beacon light levels[1]. However, optimal design of a hybrid WFS produces its own set of requirements. This was evident after the review of wavefront-sensing and AO research revealed a need for particular noise models. A summary of the identified research gaps is briefly discussed here with details and specific citations deferred to Ch. III. First, while much research has been reported on error sources in the SH WFS, none of it addressed the impact of combining sensor noise with classical intensity fluctuations such as that caused by scintillation. Also, analytical models developed for the Strehl ratio of the SRI predicted it would be insensitive to scintillation, but laboratory experiments showed that SRI performance does depend on scintillation strength. A potential reason for the disconnect between analytical work and experimental work with the SRI is that the analytical work only studied the impact of field-estimation errors, whereas experimental work can only investigate the impact of phase-estimation errors. Also, as for the SH WFS, no SRI

---

[1]Performance with extended beacons is only addressed by the inclusion of a SH WFS in the hybrid design; evaluation of hybrid performance with extended beacons is left for future work.

research has been reported that studies the combined impact of sensor noise and scintillation. Therefore, the need for new SH-WFS and SRI noise models was identified as an intermediate problem requiring solution before the specific problem of optimally designing a hybrid WFS could be properly addressed.

1.2 Proposed Solution and Approach

Because the SRI and SH WFS's perform in such complementary ways, it is natural to speculate that they may perform better if they are combined into a hybrid WFS. This dissertation reports work that evaluated whether a hybrid WFS combining a SH WFS and an SRI could perform better than either sensor alone over a range of scintillation strengths and beacon light levels.

Due to the large number of practical issues, random variables, and design parameters involved, finding the optimal approach to implementing a hybrid WFS is a difficult problem. The problem is made more difficult by the fact that a hybrid WFS requires splitting of the available light between two WFS's, which can decrease performance if not done properly. Therefore, proper design of a hybrid WFS required noise models based on a thorough analysis of the noise characteristics of each component WFS in order to ensure the optimal use of available light. As mentioned above, previously reported noise models for the SH WFS and the SRI were not sufficient for optimally designing and evaluating a hybrid WFS over a range of scintillation strengths and beacon light levels. Therefore, better models that accounted for the combined impact of sensor noise and scintillation on phase-estimation errors had to be developed before maximum-likelihood estimation techniques could be employed to design the hybrid WFS.

To maintain the highest possible degree of design flexibility, this work employed computer simulation to evaluate the performance of the hybrid WFS and compare it to a stand-alone WFS. Computer simulations, in contrast to hardware experiments, provided flexibility in design choices for hybrid architectures and enabled robust testing of the hybrid WFS's phase-estimation algorithms. Simulations were also a critical

5

part of validating the noise models developed in this work and enabled testing of the hybrid WFS over a wide range of atmospheric parameters and beacon characteristics. Furthermore, computer simulations enabled investigation of centroid error in conditions that could not be reproduced experimentally, for example photon levels that are too low to guarantee shot-noise limited performance.

1.3 Goals of Proposed Research

The specific, primary goal of this work was to combine a SH WFS with an SRI to achieve better open-loop performance than a comparable stand-alone WFS. Better performance was characterized by decreased phase errors, increased phase-estimation Strehl ratio, and decreased variation in estimation Strehl ratio (see Ch. VI). An intermediate goal of this work was the development of analytical models for photon-noise-induced phase-estimation errors for the SH and the SRI WFS's that agreed reasonably well with computer simulations. The parameter used to compare the noise models with both Monte Carlo and wave-optics simulations was error variance. For the SH WFS, the model predicted the centroid-error variance (see Ch. IV), which was converted into phase-error variance for the hybrid analysis (see Ch. VI). For the SRI, the model directly predicted phase-error variance (see Ch. V).

II. Background

Many practical issues, random variables, and design parameters are involved in determining an optimal approach to implementing an SRI/SH hybrid WFS. This chapter provides background information that was essential for properly understanding and defining this problem and ultimately developing a solution. First, to systematically address the design challenges unique to each WFS used in the hybrid WFS, computer simulation was identified as the most appropriate method for evaluating WFS performance in a variety of operating condtions. This required the methods of wave-optics, which are discussed in Sec. 2.1, to simulate the effects of atmospheric turbulence, discussed in Sec. 2.4. Also, the SRI and SH WFS's both have very different responses to photon noise and different methods of estimating phase. The details of how the SH WFS estimates phase are discussed in Sec. 2.5.1, and the SRI's function is discussed in Sec. 2.6. Optimal hybrid-WFS design also required maximum-likelihood analysis, which is discussed in Sec. 2.7. Finally, SH slope measurements must be reconstructed into phase estimates and SRI phase estimates must be unwrapped. Because wavefront reconstruction and phase unwrapping are important for effective hybrid-WFS design, they are discussed in Sec. 2.8.

2.1 Wave Optics

2.1.1 The Wave-Particle Duality of Light.
James Clerk Maxwell derived a system of vector equations that unified the theories of electricity and magnetism with mathematical elegance and suggested that light is composed of electro-magnetic (EM) waves [14, 38, 48]. Despite the astonishing accuracy of Maxwell's treatment of EM waves in predicting many observed behaviors of light, it is important to point out that some phenomena can only be accounted for by considering light as also consisting of massless particles with finite energy called photons. While experiments involving interference and diffraction have proven the classical wave nature of light, Planck's formula for blackbody radiation, Einstein's explanation of the photoelectric effect, and Compton scattering have each independently proven the particle nature

7

of light [43]. A full explanation of light propagation and its interaction with matter requires this wave-particle duality. The particle view of light best explains its emission and absorption and is therefore helpful in studying its generation and detection. Photo-detection, which is critically important to this work, requires the acknowledgement of the particle nature of light, which is best treated statistically. Therefore, this work adopts the semi-classical model of photo-electric detection, which provides a highly physical means for describing the interaction of light with matter [34]. In the semi-classical model, EM fields are treated classically (*i.e.* as a wave using Maxwell's equations) until they interact with a solid-state photodetector [34].

2.1.2 Light as an Electromagnetic Wave. As the name implies, electromagnetic waves involve the interplay of electricity and magnetism. This fact is so commonly accepted in modern times that it is easy to forget that until the work of Gauss, Ampere, and Faraday in the early 1800's, electricity and magnetism were considered to be independent of one another and in no way associated with the propagation of light. Even scientists who rejected Newton's corpuscular theory of light in favor of a wave theory thought that waves required a material medium through which to propagate [20]. But then Maxwell transformed Gauss's, Ampere's, and Faraday's work into a set of four coupled vector equations describing EM waves capable of propagating through free space and dense media [14,37]. When the particular assumptions of free space, which are discussed in greater detail in the next subsection, are applied to Maxwell's equations, they lead to a vector wave equation that shows that light propagates in vacuum at a velocity c given by

$$c = \frac{1}{\sqrt{\mu_0 \epsilon_0}}, \tag{1}$$

where ϵ_0 is the permittivity of free space (*i.e.* vacuum) and μ_0 is the permeability of free space [38]. Of course, now the symbol c is almost universally recognized as the speed of light in vacuum, but Maxwell had no reason to suspect that when he carried out the computation from Eq. (1) using values for ϵ_0 and μ_0 from work Kohlrausch and

Weber had done based solely on electrical and magnetic experiments [38]. The value he found was so close to Fizeau's measurement of the speed of light that it prompted Maxwell to suggest that, "light itself ... is an electromagnetic disturbance in the form of waves propagated through the electromagnetic field according to electromagnetic laws," (quoted by Hecht in [38]). Soon after, experiments by Hertz provided empirical evidence of this idea, and now Maxwell's equations are the accepted first principles for deriving expressions to explain the classical wave nature of light [14]. With this background as motivation, all that remains is to apply Maxwell's equations to develop useful expressions for the wave behavior of light, which is done conceptually in the following sections leaving coverage of the mathematical rigor to texts devoted to the subject (for example [14, 35, 37, 38]).

2.1.3 Wave Equations for Optics. Five fundamental quantities directly traceable to the work of Gauss, Ampere, and Faraday describe the interplay between the electric and magnetic fields. These are the electric field intensity $\boldsymbol{E}$ with units of newtons per coulomb (N/C) or equivalently volts per meter (V/m), the displacement or electric flux density $\boldsymbol{D}$ with units of C/m^2, the magnetic field intensity $\boldsymbol{H}$ with units of amperes per meter (A/m), the magnetic flux density $\boldsymbol{B}$ with units of tesla (T) or equivalently webers per square meter (Wb/m^2 = N/A·m), and the current density $\boldsymbol{J}$ with units of A/m^2 [37,77]. For a linear, homogeneous, and isotropic medium through which light propagates, these five quantities are related to one another through the material (or constitutive) relations

$$
\begin{aligned}
\boldsymbol{J} &= \sigma \boldsymbol{E}, \\
\boldsymbol{D} &= \epsilon \boldsymbol{E}, \text{and} \\
\boldsymbol{B} &= \mu \boldsymbol{H},
\end{aligned}
\tag{2}
$$

where σ is the material's electrical conductivity with units of siemens (S = V/A), μ is the material's magnetic permeability with units of N/A^2, and ϵ is the material's electrical permittivity with units of farads per meter (F/m = C/V·m) [14,77]. Maxwell's

9

equations in point form are

$$\nabla \times \boldsymbol{E} = -\frac{\partial \boldsymbol{B}}{\partial t} \tag{3}$$

$$\nabla \times \boldsymbol{H} = \boldsymbol{J} + \frac{\partial \boldsymbol{D}}{\partial t} \tag{4}$$

$$\nabla \cdot \boldsymbol{D} = \rho_v \tag{5}$$

$$\nabla \cdot \boldsymbol{B} = 0, \tag{6}$$

where $\nabla \times$ is the vector curl operator, $\nabla \cdot$ is the divergence operator, $\partial x / \partial t$ represents the time derivative of x, and ρ_v is volume charge density [37]. Equation (3) is Faraday's Law, Eq. (4) is Ampere's law modified by Maxwell to remain consistent with the continuity equation $\nabla \cdot \boldsymbol{J} = \partial \rho_v / \partial t$, Eq. (5) is Gauss's law for electric fields, and Eq. (6) is Gauss's law for magnetic fields, which is simply a statement that no magnetic monopoles have ever been found to exist in nature [20, 37].

The EM waves associated with optical wavelengths (visible to long-wave infrared) allow a few simplifying assumptions that apply in a wide range of physical conditions and allow Maxwell's equations to be combined into a single vector equation. These assumptions are

1. Any diffracting structures are large compared to the wavelength of the light.
2. Optical fields are not observed near diffracting structures (relative to wavelength).
3. The propagation medium is linear $\Rightarrow$ propagation can be treated as a linear transformation.
4. The propagation medium is homogeneous $\Rightarrow$ permittivity ϵ is constant.
5. The propagation medium is isotropic $\Rightarrow$ propagation does not depend on the direction of polarization.
6. The propagation medium is non-dispersive $\Rightarrow$ ϵ is independent of wavelength λ.
7. The propagation medium is non-magnetic $\Rightarrow$ the permeability μ is the same as for vacuum.

After applying these assumptions, Maxwell's four coupled vector equations lead to a single, second-order differential *vector wave equation* that is obeyed by both EM fields $\boldsymbol{E}$ and $\boldsymbol{H}$ as well as their associated flux densities [35, 37]. If the additional restriction is imposed that the propagating medium is also a *dielectric*, meaning it has no charges and $\boldsymbol{J} = 0$, then the vector wave equation simplifies to the immensely useful *scalar wave equation* written as

$$\nabla^2 U(\boldsymbol{r}, t) - \frac{n^2}{c^2} \frac{\partial^2}{\partial t^2} U(\boldsymbol{r}, t) = 0, \tag{7}$$

where $U(\boldsymbol{r}, t)$ is a generic scalar field that can represent any single component of the vector fields $\boldsymbol{E}$ and $\boldsymbol{H}$, ∇^2 is the Laplacian operator, n is the refractive index of the propagating medium, and as mentioned previously c is the speed of light in vacuum [14, 35]. Equation (7) is in the form of the standard differential wave equation with phase velocity given by

$$v_p = \frac{c}{n}. \tag{8}$$

The index of refraction gets its name from the method of computing it for a given material as the ratio of the angle of incidence to the angle of refraction of light passing into the material from vacuum [38]. The index of refraction is also equal to the ratio of the velocity of light in vacuum to the velocity of light in the material, so the index of refraction also gives the velocity of light traveling through the material relative to the fundamental constant c [14]. One more expression for the refractive index comes from definitions of the relative permittivity (or dielectric constant) $\epsilon_R = \epsilon/\epsilon_0$ and relative permeability $\mu_R = \mu/\mu_0$. Combining Eqs. (1) and (8) results in the refractive index expressed as

$$n = \sqrt{\epsilon_R \mu_R}. \tag{9}$$

The generic scalar field $U(\boldsymbol{r}, t)$ in Eq. (7) can refer to any of the four field quantities in Maxwell's equations under the assumptions enumerated on p. 10. Since, under these assumptions, the scalar wave equation fully describes any component of either the magnetic or electric field of an optical EM wave, $U(\boldsymbol{r}, t)$ typically symbolizes a general optical field [35].

When the light of interest is monochromatic, meaning that it consists of a single frequency ν or wavelength $\lambda = c/\nu$, the scalar wave equation becomes independent of time. The time-independent form of the scalar wave equation is called the Helmholtz equation and is written as

$$(\nabla^2 + k^2)U(\boldsymbol{r}) = 0, \tag{10}$$

where k is the magnitude of the propagation vector $\boldsymbol{k}$, which is commonly referred to as the optical wave number. The optical wave number is defined in terms of the wavelength as [14, 35]

$$k = 2\pi/\lambda. \tag{11}$$

2.1.4 The Angular Spectrum. A monochromatic plane wave propagating in free space in a direction given by the propagation vector $\boldsymbol{k}$ with direction cosines (α, β, γ) has the complex representation

$$P(x, y, z) = \exp(\mathrm{j}\boldsymbol{k} \cdot \boldsymbol{r}) = e^{\mathrm{j}\frac{2\pi}{\lambda}(\alpha x + \beta y)} e^{\mathrm{j}\frac{2\pi}{\lambda}\gamma z}, \tag{12}$$

where $\boldsymbol{r} = (x, y, z)$ is a Cartesian coordinate vector. Substituting Eq. (12) into Eq. (10) shows that a plane wave is a valid solution of the Helmholtz equation. A plane wave described by Eq. (12) is a complex sinusoid with spatial frequencies in the x and y directions given by

$$
\begin{aligned}
f_X &= \frac{\alpha}{\lambda} \\
f_Y &= \frac{\beta}{\lambda}.
\end{aligned}
\tag{13}
$$

If waves due to some unspecified system of monochromatic source(s) traveling with one component of $\boldsymbol{k}$ in the positive-z direction combine on a transverse (x, y) plane at $z = 0$, the resulting complex scalar field $U(x, y; 0)$ can be represented as the sum of

12

plane waves weighted by coefficients $A(f_X, f_Y; 0)$ over all spatial frequencies f_X and f_Y in the $z = 0$ plane [35]. This formulation adopts the convention of assigning the z axis as the optic axis and observing optical fields in planes perpendicular to the optic axis. Using Eqs. (12) and (13), the angular spectrum representation of such an optical field is given by

$$U(x, y; 0) = \int\!\!\!\int_{-\infty}^{\infty} A(f_X, f_Y; 0) \exp\left[\mathrm{j}2\pi(f_X x + f_Y y)\right] \mathrm{d}f_X \mathrm{d}f_Y, \tag{14}$$

which expresses $U(x, y; 0)$ as the inverse Fourier transform of $A(f_X, f_Y; 0)$ where the eigenfunctions are the plane waves given by $\exp[\mathrm{j}2\pi(\frac{\alpha}{\lambda}x + \frac{\beta}{\lambda}y)]$. The coefficient function $A(f_X, f_Y)$ is computed by the forward Fourier transform of $U(x, y)$ and is therefore called the *angular spectrum* of the complex field $U(x, y)$ [35].

Free-space propagation of an EM field acts as a dispersive, linear, and shift-invariant spatial filter with a transfer function given by [35]

$$H(f_X, f_Y) = \begin{cases} \exp\left[\mathrm{j}2\pi\frac{z}{\lambda}\sqrt{1 - (\lambda f_X)^2 - (\lambda f_Y)^2}\right] & , \quad \sqrt{f_X^2 + f_Y^2} < \frac{1}{\lambda} \\ 0 & , \quad \text{else.} \end{cases} \tag{15}$$

Therefore, a field propagated from $z = 0$ to some arbitrary z plane can be written in terms of the angular spectrum of $U(x, y; 0)$ as

$$U(x, y; z) = \mathcal{F}^{-1}\left\{A(f_X, f_Y; 0)H(f_X, f_Y)\right\}, \tag{16}$$

where $\mathcal{F}^{-1}\{\cdot\}$ indicates the inverse Fourier transform operation. When the wave vector $\boldsymbol{k}$ makes small angles with the optic axis, the radical term in Eq. (15) can be approximated by the first two terms of a binomial expansion [35]. This leads to a simpler form for the transfer function of free-space propagation

$$H(f_X, f_Y) = \exp(\mathrm{j}kz) \exp\left[-\mathrm{j}\pi\lambda z\left(f_X^2 + f_Y^2\right)\right]. \tag{17}$$

The assumption of small angles is called the paraxial approximation and is the same assumption required to derive many expressions in geometric ray optics. The inverse Fourier transform of Eq. (17) results in the free-space Fresnel diffraction kernel [72]. Therefore, free-space propagation that satisfies the paraxial approximation also satisfies the Fresnel approximation, and the angular spectrum propagator is equivalent to the Fresnel diffraction integral. This formulation allows analytical and numerical computation of free-space propagation of complex fields representing EM field quantities in transverse planes along the optic axis and provides the foundation of simulations performed in this work. The angular spectrum propagator fully accounts for diffraction under the previously stated assumptions and also provides the conceptual foundation for accurately modeling continuous wave-optics phenomena with discrete computer simulations [72].

2.1.5 Optical Elements and Aberrations. Defining a generalized pupil function is helpful for performing wave-optics analysis on systems with optical elements and aberrations. Generalized pupil functions are very helpful in representing atmospheric phase screens, lenses, lenslet arrays, and many other optical components and effects encountered in adaptive optics systems. The generalized pupil function $\mathcal{P}(x, y)$ is written as

$$\mathcal{P}(x, y) = P(x, y)e^{j\phi(x,y)}, \tag{18}$$

where $P(x, y)$ is a real-valued pupil function representing field amplitude attenuation effects and $\phi(x, y)$ is the phase imparted by the optical element or aberration. The pupil function often simply represents an aperture and is equal to 1 inside the pupil, 0 outside the pupil, and is set to $1/2$ at the pupil boundary to mitigate aliasing effects caused by the abrupt termination of the incident wavefront. Common pupil functions are the circ function, which defines a circular aperture, and the rect function, which is used to define rectangular apertures. For example, the pupil of a Shack-Hartmann subaperture can be approximated by a rect function, which is given along one dimension with coordinate x by [35]

$$\text{rect}(x) = \begin{cases} 1, & |x| < \frac{1}{2} \\ \frac{1}{2}, & |x| = \frac{1}{2} \\ 0, & \text{otherwise.} \end{cases} \tag{19}$$

A two-dimensional rectangle is formed simply by multiplying two one-dimensional rect functions of orthogonal coordinates. Another useful pupil function is the super-Gaussian apodization function, which generates a circular aperture with smooth edges to further mitigate aliasing effects. A super-Gaussian pupil function is generated by

$$P_{\text{sg}}(r) = \exp\left[-\left(\frac{r}{w}\right)^{\alpha}\right], \tag{20}$$

where r is a radial coordinate inside the pupil, w is the radius of the pupil, and α is some power greater than 2 that effects the extent of apodization. Higher powers cause a more abrupt transition from 1 to 0.

The phase function specifies how the optical element or aberration shapes the propagating wavefront. The phase function for optical elements can be derived from the refractive index of the element and the thickness function, which describes the physical dimensions of the element [35]. One of the most useful phase functions is the paraxial approximation for the phase of a spherical thin lens given by

$$\phi_l = -\frac{k}{2f}(x^2 + y^2), \tag{21}$$

where $k = 2\pi/\lambda$ is the scalar wave number, f is the focal length of the lens, and (x, y) is the set of transverse coordinates in the plane of the thin lens [35].

Aberrations in an optical system or propagation path can also be represented by the generalized pupil function. Aberrations are described by the aberration function $W(x, y)$, which gives the optical path difference (OPD) between the wavefront under observation and a reference wavefront. OPD is either given in meters or waves (OPD

15

in waves is computed by dividing OPD in meters by the wavelength λ). The phase function $\phi(x, y)$ has units of radians and is computed from the aberration function by

$$\phi(x, y) = 2\pi W(x, y), \tag{22}$$

for $W(x, y)$ given in waves of OPD. Aberration functions are often formed as the sum of weighted basis functions. The Seidel aberrations are components of a set formed by polynomial expansion of the aberration function about the aperture-averaged phase (i.e. the piston). The first eight Seidel aberrations are named piston, tip, tilt, defocus, astigmatism, coma, and spherical aberration [14]. Another particularly useful set of basis functions that is orthogonal on the unit circle is the set of Zernike polynomials [49].

Fourier decomposition provides another, excellent way of describing aberrations on a square pupil. Aberrations induced by the atmosphere are often represented by a Fourier series of spatial-frequency components. Relatively thick sections of the atmosphere can be represented by a single phase function (or atmospheric phase screen) as long as the optical properties of the atmosphere are approximately constant throughout. To represent atmospheric paths with changing optical properties, the path can be segmented into layers of approximately constant optical properties, and a single phase screen can be used to simulate the optical effects of each layer. This is called the layered model of atmospheric propagation. This approach was used to generate the atmospherically distorted optical fields that provided the means of testing the WFS's discussed in this work.

2.1.6 Numerical Propagation and Sampling. Atmospherically degraded optical fields result from propagation of light through a medium with an index of refraction that varies spatially in a random fashion. While a few theories exist that predict statistics for given atmospheric conditions, experimental evidence shows this theory does not always sufficiently explain the behavior of such fields, and simulations of atmospheric propagation are required to provide valid results [25, 82]. Simulating continuous physical quantities in the discrete computer environment requires careful attention to sampling. Applying Fourier analysis in such simulations requires even greater caution as quantities are transformed between spatial and spatial-frequency domains, which opens the possibility for undesired results due to aliasing. A two-dimensional, discrete signal $g_s(x, y)$ is obtained by sampling a continuous signal $g(x, y)$ through multiplication by comb functions. The comb function is defined as

$$\text{comb}(x) = \sum_{n=-\infty}^{\infty} \delta(x - n), \tag{23}$$

where x is a spatial coordinate and δ denotes the Dirac delta function [35]. Using comb functions, a discrete signal with sample spacings Δx and Δy can be written as

$$g_s(x, y) = \text{comb}\left(\frac{x}{\Delta x}\right) \text{comb}\left(\frac{y}{\Delta y}\right) g(x, y). \tag{24}$$

Fourier transforming $g_s(x, y)$ results in the convolution of the comb functions with the continuous function's spectrum, which is expressed as

$$G_s(f_X, f_Y) = \sum_{n=-\infty}^{\infty} \sum_{m=-\infty}^{\infty} G\left(f_X - \frac{n}{\Delta x}, f_Y - \frac{m}{\Delta y}\right). \tag{25}$$

This expression shows that Fourier transforming a discretely sampled continuous function produces an infinite number of spectra separated by a frequency spacing that is inversely proportional to the spatial sampling interval. Therefore, if the spatial function is not sampled finely enough, the replicas of the spectra overlap and cause aliasing. According to the Whittaker-Shannon sampling theorem, a bandlimited continuous function can be perfectly reconstructed from the sampled function as long

17

as

$$\Delta x \leq \frac{1}{2B_x}$$

$$\text{and} \tag{26}$$

$$\Delta y \leq \frac{1}{2B_y},$$

where B_x and B_y are the finite bandwidths of the continuous function in the x and y directions [35].

A further restriction imposed by discrete sampling is that the source must be confined to a finite spatial extent, which causes rippling in the spectra [16]. The ripples become larger as the spatial extent of the source becomes smaller, so numerical wave-optics simulations require careful analysis of the trade-off between the size of the simulation grid, the sample size in the source plane, the sample size in the observation plane, and the number of samples across the simulation grid. These constraints can be relaxed by implementing multiple-partial-propagation techniques and absorbing boundaries [72]. When multiple partial propagations are used, additional partial propagations with shorter distances between them can decrease the grid size requirements while still meeting the sample size requirements in the source and observation planes. Partial propagations provide the added benefit of implementing a layered atmospheric turbulence model by allowing the application of generalized pupil functions at partial propagation planes [72].

2.1.7 Validity of Wave Optics Simulations.   Simulated complex EM fields generated with wave-optics techniques require validation to ensure sampling constraints are adequately met. Simulations in this work generate optical test fields by numerically propagating a point source through a layered model of atmospheric turbulence using a multiple-partial-propagation implementation of the angular spectrum. The sample spacing, grid size, propagation distances, and number of propagation steps are carefully analyzed to meet the identified sampling constraints. The first step in validating the chosen simulation parameters is comparison of the simulation results to the analytical results for Fresnel propagation. Propagation of a point source can be modeled by using the Fresnel diffraction transfer function of Eq. (17) in Eq. (16) and setting the field at $z = 0$ to a Kronecker delta, which has an infinite-bandwidth, uniform-amplitude spectrum. Evaluating the inverse Fourier transform in Eq. (16) leads to the analytical expression for an optical field due to propagation of a point source from its location at $z = 0$ to an observation plane at some arbitrary z location, which, in the paraxial approximation to a spherical wave, is given by

$$U(x, y) = \frac{e^{jkz}}{j\lambda z} \exp\left[j\frac{k}{2z}(x^2 + y^2)\right].$$

(27)

Simulation of a true point source is impossible because of the infinite bandwidth. However, it is possible to numerically propagate a slightly extended source that matches the analytical results for a point source very closely within some specified region of interest. For a $D \times D$ square region of interest located a distance z from the source plane with transverse coordinates (ξ, η), a point source can be approximated as [72]

$$\tilde{U}_{ps}(\xi, \eta) = e^{-j\frac{k}{2z}(\xi^2 + \eta^2)} \left(\frac{D}{\lambda z}\right)^2 \mathrm{sinc}\left(\frac{D}{\lambda z}\xi\right) \mathrm{sinc}\left(\frac{D}{\lambda z}\eta\right),$$

(28)

where

$$\mathrm{sinc}(x) \triangleq \frac{\sin(\pi x)}{\pi x}.$$

(29)

Figures 2 (a) and (b) show the irradiance[1] and phase resulting from analytical propagation of a point source through vacuum. Figures 2 (c) and (d) show the irradiance and phase resulting from numerical propagation of a simulated point source through vacuum. The dashed, blue square in (c) and solid black square in (d) show the observation-plane region of interest on the irradiance and phase, respectively, of the

---

[1]The terms *irradiance* [W/m^2] and *intensity* [W/sr] are sometimes used interchangeably throughout this document and should both be understood generally as the distribution of power over a spatial extent; the distinction is simply a matter of units, which should be able to be inferred from the context when units are important.

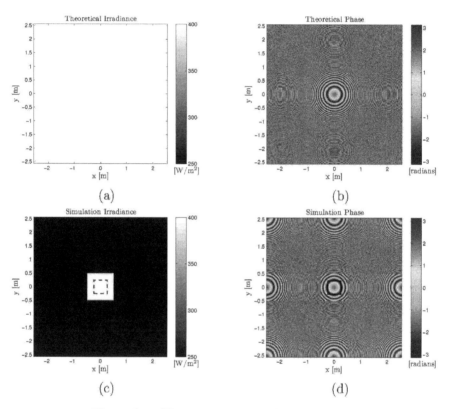

Figure 2: Vacuum-propagated point source

simulation results. In this region, the simulation results and analytical results match very closely. The phase from the simulation shows the aliasing caused by finite sampling, but this aliasing is kept from corrupting the region of interest because proper sampling and partial-propagation distances were carefully chosen based on a thorough sampling analysis.

2.2 Optical Coherence

The preceding development of wave-optics methods assumed monochromatic, *i.e.* single-frequency, light. However, light from a physical source is never monochromatic but has rapidly changing amplitude and phase [14]. Even laser light oscillates at different temporal frequencies ν, although it has a sufficiently narrow bandwidth of frequencies $\Delta\nu$ around some central frequency ν_0 that it can be approximated as monochromatic. Such light is called quasimonochromatic [34].

The amplitude and phase oscillations of light emitted from a single source at a given moment in time t are generally correlated with those of light emitted at some later time $t + \tau$ provided the time delay τ is small enough. Also, the oscillations of light at a given point in space r in an optical disturbance propagated from a single source are generally correlated with those of nearby points in the optical field. The correlation between oscillations of light at two points separated in time or space is called coherence.

Because the oscillations of EM waves in the infrared and visible regions of the spectrum are far too fast to be tracked by any real detector, coherence is measured using interference phenomena. In fact, interference phenomena motivated the wave theory of light, which is fundamental to the concept of coherence. Historically, amplitude-splitting interferometers, such as the Michelson interferometer, have been used to characterize the temporal coherence of light, whereas wavefront-splitting interference, such as that imposed by Young's double-slit experiment, has provided insight into the spatial coherence of light [14, 34]. The details of these two experiments are left to more rigorous texts on the subject, *e.g.* Refs. [14], [34], and [38].

Here it is sufficient to summarize the analysis that develops a single expression that fully characterizes both temporal and spatial coherence, namely the *mutual coherence function* (MCF). The MCF is foundational to wavefront sensing for atmospherically degraded optical fields. It is a function of the coherence time Δt_c, which is important for interferometric wavefront sensing, and it also depends on coherence width, which is specified for the atmosphere by Fried's parameter r_0.

Describing the MCF begins with consideration of two optical disturbances at two different moments in time t and $t + \tau$ and two different points in space $\boldsymbol{r}_1$ and $\boldsymbol{r}_2$, represented by complex values $U_1(\boldsymbol{r}_1, t)$ and $U_2(\boldsymbol{r}_2, t + \tau)$. The MCF is the temporal and spatial correlation between U_1 and U_2 given by

$$\Gamma(|\boldsymbol{r}_1 - \boldsymbol{r}_2|, \tau) \triangleq \langle U_1(\boldsymbol{r}_1, t) U_2^*(\boldsymbol{r}_2, t + \tau) \rangle_T, \tag{30}$$

where the angle brackets with subscript T represent a time average [14, 34, 38]. A convenient shorthand notation for the MCF is $\Gamma_{12}(\tau)$, which uses the subscript $_{12}$ to indicate that the MCF is describing the coherence between optical disturbances at two different points in space $\boldsymbol{r}_1$ and $\boldsymbol{r}_2$ [14, 34, 38]. The MCF, by definition, is a statistical quantity, and the time average indicated in Eq. (30) requires that the statistics of U_1 and U_2 are ergodic. If this is not the case, then the time average must be replaced with an ensemble average (see Ref. [34] Sec. 7.5). The complex degree of coherence is a common measure of the correlation of optical disturbances at two points separated by time τ and distance $|\boldsymbol{r}_1 - \boldsymbol{r}_2|$ and is given by

$$\gamma_{12}(\tau) \triangleq \frac{\Gamma_{12}(\tau)}{\sqrt{\Gamma_{11}(0)\Gamma_{22}(0)}}. \tag{31}$$

The definitions in Eqs. (30) and (31) imply the two different types of coherence mentioned previously. *Temporal coherence* is described by the degree of coherence $|\gamma_{12}(\tau)|$, which is a function of the temporal separation τ of the optical disturbances. *Spatial coherence* is described by the coherence factor $|\mu_{12}| = |\gamma_{12}(0)|$ between two points $\boldsymbol{r}_1$ and $\boldsymbol{r}_2$ at a single moment in time.

For an optical disturbance at a single point in space, the degree of coherence provides a means of specifying the coherence time as a measure of temporal coherence. The coherence time is given by

$$\Delta t_c = \int\limits_{-\infty}^{\infty} |\gamma(\tau)|^2 \mathrm{d}\tau. \tag{32}$$

The degree of (self) coherence is related to the normalized power spectral density (PSD) of light through the Wiener-Khinchin theorem [34]. Therefore, the coherence time can be computed for light from a source with a known PSD, or spectral line, which provides a measure of power as a function of the average optical frequency ν and the optical bandwidth $\Delta\nu$. For example, a source with a Gaussian PSD, such as light from a low-pressure gas discharge lamp, has coherence time $\tau_c = 0.664/\Delta\nu$ [34]. For a source with a Lorentzian line, such as light from a high-pressure gas discharge lamp, $\tau_c = 0.318/\Delta\nu$ [34]. Because the coherence time is inversely proportional to the optical bandwidth, it is often convenient to simply use a rectangular line for the PSD, in which case $\tau_c = 1/\Delta\nu$. The coherence time grows infinitely large as the bandwidth becomes small, so that monochromatic light has perfect temporal coherence and temporally incoherent light contains many optical frequencies. Quasimonochromatic light, such as laser light, is effectively temporally coherent because it has a small enough bandwidth to make the coherence time infinitely large for all practical purposes.

Spatial coherence is exhibited to a high degree by light from a single point source and is very important to imaging quality. It is also greatly affected by the properties of the propagation medium. The spatial-coherence width defines the maximum distance separating two optical disturbances that can still be considered to be mutually coherent. The coherence width is related to the isoplanatic patch size of an imaging system or propagation medium. The size of the isoplanatic patch imposes a limit on the size of an object for which the assumption of shift invariance for a given transfer function applies [35]. This transfer function could be that of the propagating

23

medium, e.g. the atmosphere, or that of an optical system [34, 35]. When $\tau = 0$ and $\boldsymbol{r}_1 = \boldsymbol{r}_2$, the MCF $\Gamma_{11}(0)$ is simply the irradiance of the optical field at time t and point $\boldsymbol{r}_1$. When spatial coherence at a single instance in time is of primary concern, the MCF simplifies to the mutual intensity function $J_{12} = \Gamma_{12}(0)$, and the complex coherence factor $\mu_{12} \triangleq \gamma_{12}(0)$ replaces the complex degree of coherence. In terms of mutual intensity, the coherence factor is formally given by

$$|\mu_{12}| \triangleq |\gamma_{12}(0)| = \frac{|J_{12}|}{\sqrt{I(\boldsymbol{r}_1)I(\boldsymbol{r}_2)}}, \tag{33}$$

where $I(\boldsymbol{r}_1)$ and $I(\boldsymbol{r}_2)$ are the values of the irradiance at the points $\boldsymbol{r}_1$ and $\boldsymbol{r}_2$ [34]. When the coherence factor is identically equal to zero, the optical disturbances at $\boldsymbol{r}_1$ and $\boldsymbol{r}_2$ are said to be mutually *incoherent* [34] (p. 182). When $|\mu_{12}| = 1$, the disturbances are perfectly correlated and considered to be mutually *coherent* [34] (p. 183). When $0 < |\mu_{12}| < 1$, the disturbances are in a state of partial coherence, quantified by their degree of coherence $|\gamma_{12}(\tau)|$ [14, 34, 38].

Wave-optics methods can be applied to incoherent light by analyzing individual frequencies independently and then summing the results according to the superposition principle [35, 92]. Also, incoherent imaging can be analyzed using frequency analysis and the idea that an incoherent image is the result of convolving the geometric image of an object with the point spread function (PSF) of the imaging system or the impulse response of the propagating medium [34, 35].

2.3 Photodetection Statistics

In the semi-classical approach to photo-detection, light is assumed to propagate classically until hits a photodetector. The absorption of light energy by the photodetector material and subsequent transport and emission of an excited electron are then described statistically. A photoevent is the release from the surface of the detector material of an electron that was excited by a photon [34]. The number of photoevents K in a defined area that occur during a specific time interval is referred to as the photocount [34]. Photoevents obey Poisson statistics, so they have a probability function given by

$$P(K) = \frac{\left(\bar{K}\right)^K}{K!} \exp\left(-\bar{K}\right), \tag{34}$$

where $\bar{K}$ is the mean photocount and ! represents the factorial operation.

Because photoevents are fundamentally stochastic quantities, anytime light with random fluctuations in the classical intensity is detected, the process is doubly stochastic. Therefore, the statistical behavior of the interaction of light with matter is governed by the nature of the light involved. At one extreme, thermal light contains many wavelengths and has a very short coherence time. At the other extreme, laser light has a very small optical bandwidth and a very long coherence time. However, significant amplitude fluctuations in laser light can cause it to behave more like thermal light, in which case it is sometimes referred to as pseudothermal light [34]. The mean and variance of detector photocounts K for thermal or pseudothermal light are given by [34]

$$\langle K \rangle = \frac{\eta_q}{h\bar{\nu}}\mathcal{W}; \tag{35}$$

$$\sigma_K^2 = \frac{\eta_q}{h\bar{\nu}}\mathcal{W} + \left(\frac{\eta_q}{h\bar{\nu}}\right)^2 \sigma_W^2, \tag{36}$$

where η_q is the detector quantum efficiency, $h = 6.626196 \times 10^{-34}$ [joules$\times$seconds] is Planck's constant, $\bar{\nu}$ is the average optical frequency of the light, $\mathcal{W}$ is the irradiance integrated over the detector area A_d (or, equivalently, the intensity integrated over the detector solid angle) and integration time T_d of the detector, and σ_W^2 is the variance of the classical irradiance fluctuations.

The probability function for the photocounts of polarized thermal light follows a negative binomial distribution, which can be expressed in terms of gamma distributions and the count degeneracy parameter δ_c as [34]

$$P(K) = \frac{\Gamma\left(K + \frac{\bar{K}}{\delta_c}\right)}{K!\Gamma\left(\frac{\bar{K}}{\delta_c}\right)} \left[(1+\delta_c)^{\bar{K}/\delta_c} \left(1 + \frac{1}{\delta_c}\right)^K\right]^{-1}. \tag{37}$$

When the degeneracy parameter approaches zero, this function simplifies to the Poisson distribution [34]. Also, for polarized thermal light, the photocount variance can be written in terms of the degeneracy parameter as

$$\sigma_K^2 = \langle K \rangle \left(1 + \delta_c\right). \tag{38}$$

The degeneracy parameter accounts for classical fluctuations in the irradiance and is defined as

$$\delta_c = \frac{\bar{K}}{\mathcal{M}}, \tag{39}$$

where $\mathcal{M}$ is a parameter that describes the number of degrees of freedom of the irradiance within a single coherence time and coherence area. For cross-spectrally pure light, $\mathcal{M}$ can be expressed as the product of the temporal degrees of freedom $\mathcal{M}_t$ and the spatial degrees of freedom $\mathcal{M}_s$ [34]. For integration times much shorter than the coherence time, the temporal degrees of freedom parameter decreases with an increasing degree of coherence but can never be less than one [34]. For integration times much longer than the coherence time, the number of temporal degrees of freedom is equal to the number of coherence intervals contained in the integration time [34]. The spatial degrees of freedom parameter behaves similarly relative to the coherence area [34]. Equation (39) shows that as $\mathcal{M}$ becomes large relative to the number of photocounts, *i.e* the number of photoevents occurring in a given detector area during a given time interval, δ_c approaches zero, and photocount statistics are well approximated by the Poisson distribution. Intensity fluctuations can be assumed to be minimal during the integration time either for point-source beacons with very long coherence times or for pseudothermal beacons with short coherence times relative to the integration time [34]. In the second case, for atmospheric wavefront-sensing applications, the

26

coherence time of pseudothermal beacons must be long enough to avoid classical intensity fluctuations but short enough to allow the integration of intensity to occur faster than the temporal evolution of atmospheric phase disturbances [87]. Similarly, detector areas should be large enough that classical intensity fluctuations are averaged out over their area while being small enough to adequately sample atmospheric wavefront distortions.

2.4   *Atmospheric Turbulence*

A layered theory of atmospheric turbulence can be combined with free-space wave-optics simulations to model the propagation of light through a turbulent atmosphere, which is critical in analyzing the effectiveness of hybrid wavefront sensing techniques explored in this work. The impact of atmospheric turbulence on optical fields is characterized by the MCF (see Sec. 2.2), which is closely related to the wave structure function $D_\psi(r)$ that inherits its qualities from the refractive-index structure of the atmosphere. Stochastic solutions of Maxwell's equations provide estimates for these important statistical measures of turbulence-degraded optical fields. Additionally, three statistical atmospheric parameters are useful in characterizing optical effects of atmospheric turbulence. These are the atmospheric coherence width r_0, the log-amplitude variance σ_χ^2, and the isoplanatic angle θ_0. This section provides a high-level overview of the statistical concepts used to define these quantities, which describe the optical impact of atmospheric turbulence.

2.4.1   The Optical Structure of the Atmosphere.   The refractive index of air is very nearly unity, and if the atmosphere was completely still and had the same refractive index everywhere, propagation through it could be treated as free-space propagation. However, air in the Earth's atmosphere is never perfectly still but behaves as a viscous fluid with both laminar and turbulent flow [9]. Also, variation of air density with altitude causes the refractive index to also vary with altitude. Furthermore, temperature fluctuations and turbulent mixing induce random behavior

27

in the atmosphere's index of refraction [1]. Because the refractive-index fluctuations are small (much less than one), the index of refraction of the atmosphere can be expressed as a function of a point in space r and moment in time t as

$$n(\boldsymbol{r}, t) = n_0 + n_1(\boldsymbol{r}, t), \tag{40}$$

where $n_0 = \langle n(\boldsymbol{r}, t) \rangle \cong 1$ is the mean value of $n(\boldsymbol{r}, t)$ and $n_1(\boldsymbol{r}, t)$ represents the random fluctuations of $n(\boldsymbol{r}, t)$ about its mean value [1]. Taylor's frozen flow hypothesis assumes light propagates through turbulence much faster than the flow of the turbulence, so changes in atmospheric quantities at an observation point are only caused by the atmosphere moving across that point rather than from local changes in the quantities. Therefore, temporally evolving atmospheric turbulence can be modeled by translating an atmospheric phase screen across the field of view [1]. Under the assumptions of quasimonochromatic light and Taylor's frozen flow hypothesis, the time dependence in Eq. (40) is dropped and n_0 becomes a function of position alone.

Refractive-index fluctuations in the atmosphere occur over a varying range of scale sizes measured in units of meters. Wind shear and convection cause large-scale refractive-index fluctuations with a lower bound given by the outer scale L_0; typically $L_0 \gtrsim 10\mathrm{m}$ [1]. The region below the smallest scale size is referred to as the dissipation range and has an upper bound defined by the inner scale l_0. In the dissipation range, turbulence dissipates and air flow becomes laminar. The range of scale sizes between the inner and outer scales is referred to as the inertial subrange because inertial forces dominate. These forces cause the air flow to become turbulent, which sets up a random spatial distribution of regions of varying sizes, each with different values of refractive index [1]. Regions over which the refractive index remains approximately constant are called eddies and range in size from several millimeters to several meters in diameter [1].

Far from flow boundaries or heat sources, the random distribution of eddies well inside the inertial subrange ($l_0 \ll l \ll L_0$) is assumed to be statistically isotropic

28

and locally homogeneous [1,71]. This type of behavior characterizes a *turbulent atmosphere*, and the remaining theory in this section only applies where statistical isotropy and local homogeneity can safely be assumed. Because statistical homogeneity is only locally assumed, covariance functions are replaced by structure functions, which are the mean-square value of the difference of a quantity at two points [71]. The structure function for the index of refraction is defined as

$$D_n(\boldsymbol{r}_1, \boldsymbol{r}_2) = \left\langle [n(\boldsymbol{r}_1) - n(\boldsymbol{r}_2)]^2 \right\rangle, \tag{41}$$

where $\boldsymbol{r}_1 = (x_1, y_1, z_1)$ and $\boldsymbol{r}_2 = (x_2, y_2, z_2)$ are coordinate vectors for two different locations, and angle brackets indicate an ensemble average. The assumption of local homogeneity allows the refractive-index structure function to be expressed as a function of the vector distance $\boldsymbol{r}_1 - \boldsymbol{r}_2$, and the assumption of isotropic turbulence further simplifies the structure function so that it depends only on the scalar distance $r = |\boldsymbol{r}_1 - \boldsymbol{r}_2|$ [9]. Therefore, the structure function of the refractive index of a homogeneous and isotropic atmosphere is often symbolized by $D_n(r)$.

The strength of turbulence is characterized by structure constants for various atmospheric parameters of interest. Kolmogorov applied dimensional analysis based on a set of hypotheses grounded in physical intuition to develop an expression for the longitudinal structure function of wind velocity in a turbulent atmosphere based on the velocity structure constant C_v^2 [9]. Corrsin and Obhukov extended Kolmogorov's theory of structure functions to conservative passive scalars, which enabled development of the potential temperature structure function $D_\theta(r)$ in terms of the potential temperature structure constant C_θ^2. Optical turbulence is characterized by the refractive-index structure constant C_n^2, which is a function of the potential temperature and specific humidity [9]. The refractive-index structure function is defined in the inertial subrange as

$$D_n(r) = C_n^2 r^{2/3} , \quad l_0 \ll r \ll L_0 . \tag{42}$$

This expression for the refractive-index structure function is identical to that for potential temperature expressed as a function of C_θ^2, which is based on the assumption that refractive-index fluctuations are caused almost exclusively by temperature variations, allowing pressure and humidity variations to be neglected [1]. Since both of these structure functions follow the same two-thirds power law Kolmogorov developed for the velocity structure function, optical turbulence in the inertial subrange is often referred to as Kolmogorov turbulence.

The optical turbulence spectrum $\Phi_n(\kappa)$ describes the refractive-index fluctuations as a function of angular spatial frequency[2] κ and comes from applying a three-dimensional Fourier transform to the covariance function of the refractive-index fluctuations $B_n(\boldsymbol{r})$. When atmospheric turbulence is isotropic and locally homogeneous, $\Phi_n(\kappa)$ can be related to the refractive-index structure function. For Kolmogorov turbulence this results in an optical-turbulence power spectrum given by [9]

$$\Phi_n(\kappa) \;=\; 0.033 C_n^2 \kappa^{-11/3} \quad , \quad \tfrac{1}{L_0} \ll \kappa \ll \tfrac{1}{l_0}. \tag{43}$$

Although other expressions for the power spectrum of atmospheric turbulence have been derived for use when the effect of inner and outer scale cannot be neglected, inside the inertial subrange they reduce to the Kolmogorov spectrum [1]. Because of its simple form and the wide applicability of the assumption that turbulence is restricted to the inertial subrange, the Kolmogorov spectrum is sufficient for analysis in this work.

As a final note on the optical structure of the atmosphere, refractive-index structure constant profiles $C_n^2(h)$ have been generated by measuring the temperature difference between two points separated by a known distance over a range of altitudes h in a variety of locations, times of day, and weather conditions [1]. C_n^2 is generally a strong function of altitude but is constant for horizontal propagation paths that are

---

[2]This is the spatial analog to angular frequency ω, i.e. $\kappa = 2\pi\rho$ in radians per meter, where $\rho = (f_X, f_Y, f_Z)$ is a three-dimensional spatial-frequency coordinate vector with units of cycles per meter [9].

short relative to the radius of the earth. This work generally assumes a constant C_n^2 profile since it simplifies equations and does not detract from wavefront sensor design requirements.

2.4.2 Optical Turbulence Statistics.   Monochromatic light propagating through a material medium with spatially distributed random fluctuations of the index of refraction $n(\boldsymbol{r})$ can be described by the stochastic Helmoltz equation (a result of Maxwell's equations) as

$$\left[\nabla^2 + k^2 n^2(\boldsymbol{r})\right] U(\boldsymbol{r}) = 0. \tag{44}$$

When localized pockets, or eddies, of relatively constant refractive index are defined as the diffracting structures, the first two assumptions of Sec. 2.1 remain valid for optical and infrared wavelengths in the inertial subrange of the atmosphere since the wavelengths are much smaller than the inner scale of the turbulence [1]. The last assumption of Sec. 2.1 also remains valid since transparent media are non-magnetic [14]. The assumption of linearity applies in nearly all cases of propagation through air except for high-power laser beam propagation [93]. Also, although the atmosphere is a dispersive medium, the scale of atmospheric dispersion allows it to be neglected when considering diffractive effects under the assumption of quasimonochromatic light [71]. Furthermore, atmospheric effects on polarization are negligible, so the assumption of material isotropy remains valid [1, 80]. However, the assumption of homogeneity no longer applies since the index of refraction is now considered to be a random field. This requires a stochastic approach to solving Eq. (44) that accounts for the random refractive-index fluctuations $n_1(\boldsymbol{r})$.

One method of solving the stochastic Helmholtz equation is through the classical Rytov method, which assumes a solution of the form

$$\begin{aligned} U(\boldsymbol{r}, L) &= U_0(\boldsymbol{r}, L) \exp[\psi(\boldsymbol{r}, L)] \\ &= U_0(\boldsymbol{r}, L) \exp[\psi_1(\boldsymbol{r}, L) + \psi_2(\boldsymbol{r}, L) + \ ... \ ], \end{aligned} \tag{45}$$

where $U_0(\boldsymbol{r}, L)$ is the two-dimensional field with transverse vector spatial coordinate $\boldsymbol{r} = (x, y)$ and is due to free-space propagation of an optical wave a distance L along the z-axis. The argument $\psi(\boldsymbol{r}, L)$ is the total complex perturbation of the field due to random inhomogeneities along the propagation path [1]. To make the solution tractable, complex perturbations are represented as the sum of successively smaller perturbations [71]. The first- and second-order perturbations ψ_1 and ψ_2 are shown in Eq. (45). The perturbation ψ is a complex random variable and can be written as $\psi = \chi + \mathrm{j}S$. Substituting this expression for ψ into Eq. (45) expresses the optical field as

$$
\begin{aligned}
U(\boldsymbol{r}, L) &= U_0(\boldsymbol{r}, L) \exp\left[\chi(\boldsymbol{r}, L) + \mathrm{j}S(\boldsymbol{r}, L)\right] \\
&= U_0(\boldsymbol{r}, L) \exp\left[\chi(\boldsymbol{r}, L)\right] \exp\left[\mathrm{j}S(\boldsymbol{r}, L)\right],
\end{aligned}
\tag{46}
$$

which illustrates why χ is referred to as the log-amplitude fluctuations of the optical field and S represents the phase perturbations. The statistics of χ and S are determined from the statistics of the refractive-index fluctuations n_1, which are randomly distributed with zero mean [9]. Furthermore, χ and S are formed from the sum of a large number of fluctuations of n along the propagation path [9]. Therefore, by the central-limit theorem, χ and S are zero-mean Gaussian random variables, which makes ψ also a Gaussian (normally-distributed) random variable.

Since ψ is a normally-distributed random function of the refractive-index fluctuations, the first-, second-, and fourth-order moments of the random field $U(\boldsymbol{r}, L)$ can be expressed exactly in terms of ψ_1 and ψ_2 and the atmospheric turbulence spectrum $\Phi_n(\kappa, z)$ [1]. The first moment of the field is its mean value $\langle U(\boldsymbol{r}, L) \rangle$, and the second moment is the MCF $\Gamma_{12}(L)$ [1].[3] The coherence factor $|\mu_{12}|$ is a normalized form of the MCF that provides a measure of the spatial coherence of an optical field (see

---

[3]The MCF discussed in this section is equivalent to the MCF $\Gamma_{12}(\tau)$ discussed in Sec. 2.2 with the additional restriction that the two points of observation are in the same transverse plane at $z = L$ and at the same point in time, i.e. $\tau = 0$. The notation used here borrows that of Andrews and Phillips to explicitly show the MCF as a function of propagation distance L and indicate that the observation points are in the same transverse plane [1].

Sec. 2.2). When $|\mu_{12}| = 1$, the values of the field at the two points $\boldsymbol{r}_1$ and $\boldsymbol{r}_2$ are perfectly coherent, and when $|\mu_{12}| = 0$ they are perfectly incoherent.

In an isotropic and homogeneous random field, the coherence factor μ_{12} is a function only of the distance $r = |\boldsymbol{r}_1 - \boldsymbol{r}_2|$. For optical fields atmospherically propagated a distance L, the coherence factor is related to the wave structure function $D_\psi(r, L)$ by [1]

$$|\mu(r, L)| = \exp\left[-\frac{1}{2}D_\psi(r, L)\right]. \tag{47}$$

The distance r associated with the $1/e$ value of the coherence factor is called the spatial coherence radius ρ_0 [1]. The Rytov approximation leads to expressions for the MCF in terms of the wave structure function, which can be computed from the turbulence spectrum $\Phi_n(\kappa)$ to provide a measure of ρ_0.

Fried's parameter r_0 provides a more intuitively useful measure of coherence than ρ_0, since it is based on the impact of atmospheric turbulence on imaging quality. Incoherent imaging data from the 1960's showed a limit to achievable resolution from increasing the aperture diameter of a telescope in the presence of atmospheric turbulence. Fried defined resolution as the integral over the two-dimensional spatial-frequency domain of the modulation transfer function (MTF) of an imaging system, which he expressed in terms of the wave structure function of atmospherically propagated EM waves [27]. His expression showed an absolute limit to the resolution of an imaging system in the presence of atmospheric distortions, which is the resolution achievable by an otherwise-diffraction-limited imaging system with aperture diameter equal to r_0 [27]. Fried's parameter r_0 is associated with the average coherence width of the eddies of atmospheric turbulence, which is why it is also referred to as the atmospheric coherence width. The wave structure function can be expressed as a function of r_0 and is given for the case of Kolmogorov turbulence by [27]

$$D_\psi(r) = 6.88 \left(\frac{r}{r_0}\right)^{5/3}. \tag{48}$$

This leads to the expression for r_0 computed from integrating C_n^2 over the propagation path, i.e. [71]

$$r_0 = \left[0.423k^2 \int_0^L C_n^2(z)\gamma^{5/3}\mathrm{d}z \right]^{-3/5}, \tag{49}$$

where γ is a *propagation parameter* that depends on the form of the wavefront with $\gamma = 1$ for a plane wave, and

$$\gamma = \frac{|R_0 - z|}{|R_0 - L|}$$

for a spherical wave with radius of curvature $R_0 \neq L$ [71]. The atmospheric coherence width and spatial coherence radius are related to each other by $r_0 = 2.1\rho_0$ [1]. The expression for r_0 in Eq. (49) applies for a plane wave or spherical wave propagating from $z = 0$ to $z = L$ as well as for a plane wave or spherical wave propagating from $z = L$ to $z = 0$.

Another parameter that characterizes atmospheric turbulence in terms of imaging system performance is the isoplanatic angle θ_0, which is computed from C_n^2 by [71]

$$\theta_0 = \left[2.91k^2 \int_0^L C_n^2(z)z^{5/3}\mathrm{d}z \right]^{-3/5}. \tag{50}$$

The isoplanatic angle is useful when considering extended sources because it gives the resolution limit caused by atmospheric turbulence in terms of the field of view of the imaging system.

The fourth-order moment of the random field $U(\boldsymbol{r}, L)$ is the cross-coherence function $\Gamma_{1234}(L)$ and can be used to develop expressions for the normalized irradiance variance, also called the scintillation index, $\tilde{\sigma}_I^2$ [1]. The scintillation index characterizes the irradiance fluctuations caused by atmospheric turbulence and is computed by

$$\tilde{\sigma}_I^2 = \frac{\sigma_I^2}{\langle I \rangle^2}, \tag{51}$$

where σ_I^2 is the variance of the intensity, and $\langle I \rangle$ is the mean intensity. For Gaussian fields, the scintillation index can be decomposed into on-axis and radial components [1]. However, this work is primarily concerned with spherical and plane waves, which are limiting cases of Gaussian fields for which the radial component of the scintillation index disappears [1]. The theoretical expression for the log-amplitude variance σ_χ^2 is called the Rytov number, which for either a spherical or plane wave propagating through weak Kolmogorov turbulence along the z-axis from $z = 0$ to $z = L$ is given by [71]

$$\sigma_\chi^2 = 0.5631k^{7/6} \int_0^L C_n^2(z)(L-z)^{5/6}\gamma^{5/6}\mathrm{d}z. \tag{52}$$

Propagation from $z = L$ to $z = 0$, simply requires substitution for $(L - z)$ with z in Eq. (52) to get [71]

$$\sigma_\chi^2 = 0.5631k^{7/6} \int_0^L C_n^2(z)(\gamma z)^{5/6}\mathrm{d}z. \tag{53}$$

In weak scintillation ($\sigma_\chi^2 \leq 0.25$), the log-amplitude variance is approximately four times the log-intensity variance $\sigma_{\ln I}^2$, which is sometimes also referred to as the Rytov variance [71].

2.5 The Shack-Hartmann Wavefront Sensor

The Shack-Hartmann WFS has been in use for a long time, and the AO community has learned and written much about its capabilities and limitations. It is based on the well-documented and proven Hartmann test. The Hartmann test, invented by J. Hartmann in 1900, uses a screen with holes in it placed in a converging beam near focus to determine surface irregularities of an optical element under test by measuring the displacement of the resulting focused spots from those measured for a reference surface [45]. In 1971 B. C. Platt and R. V. Shack proposed using a lenticular screen made with two identical layers of cylindrical lenses placed at the pupil plane instead of a screen with holes [74]. Such an arrangement is most often referred to as a

Shack-Hartmann WFS. Modern Shack-Hartmann sensors use a lenslet array formed from a solid piece of optical material instead of a lenticular screen [45]. The lenslet array effectively segments the incident wavefront and focuses the resulting samples at a common image plane where transverse spot displacements are measured and used to estimate the wavefront gradient inside the pupil. In many cases the wavefront can be very accurately estimated simply by integrating these gradient measurements [45]. Often the integration is performed using least-squares reconstruction of the gradients into phase estimates.

2.5.1 Theory. A simple tilt sensor consists of a lens and a detector array. The displacement of a focused spot from the center of the detector array can provide an estimate for the tilt of a wave incident on the focusing lens. Figure 3 shows a diagram of such a tilt sensor. A plane wave incident on a positive thin lens with diameter d is focused onto a detector at the focal plane located a distance f behind the lens. This plane wave can be represented as a bundle of parallel rays brought to focus by the lens at a point at the center of the focal plane. The rays and the corresponding perpendicular wavefront are shown in Fig. 3 as dashed lines for a normally incident wavefront. A plane wave tilted from normal by an angle θ_T measured above the optic axis is focused at the detector a transverse distance T below the on-axis spot of the normally incident plane wave or reference wave. The rays and wavefront of the tilted plane wave are shown as solid lines in Fig. 3.

The distance W along a line parallel to the optic axis between a point on the reference wave and a point on the tilted wave represents the OPD between the two points on the respective wavefronts. The slope of the incoming plane wave is defined as the change in OPD with respect to the change in the transverse coordinate y. Assuming small changes in W with respect to changes in y, this simple development from geometric optics relates the transverse displacement of the spot in the focal plane

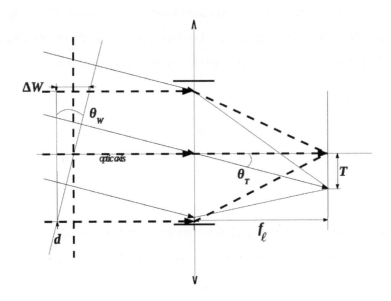

Figure 3:   Tilt sensor
A lens with diameter d and a detector located one focal length f after the lens measure the spot displacement T, from which the tilt angle θ and the wavefront slope dW/dy can be computed.

to the slope dW/dy of the incoming plane by

$$\theta_T = \frac{dW}{dy} = -\frac{T}{f_\ell}, \tag{54}$$

which gives the tilt angle of the incident wavefront in units of radians. Another view of this effect comes from Fourier optics. A lens is a physical implementation of a Fourier transform, and accordingly, a pure tilt in the lens plane results in a shift in the focal plane [35]. Therefore, a tilted plane wave incident on a lens results in a spot displacement $T = fs$, where $s = dW/dy$ is the slope of the wavefront and f is the focal length of the lens [7].

A SH sensor combines a monolithic lenslet array with a detector array to form an array of tightly packed tilt sensors. Each lenslet forms a subaperture that samples a small portion of the incident wavefront. The subapertures of a SH WFS are square with side length d. If the subapertures are small enough, each subaperture wavefront sample is well approximated by a tilted plane wave. The arrays of tilts in the x and y directions are therefore a measure of the two-dimensional wavefront gradient averaged over the subapertures and can be reconstructed into phase estimates for the incident wavefront.

   2.5.2 Measuring Spot Displacement.   Several methods are used to measure the displacement of the focal spot of each subaperture from the on-axis position. Two of these methods, the quad-cell detector and the centroid detector are discussed here. The quad-cell detector is divided into quadrants as shown in Fig. 4. Each quadrant is a stand-alone detector that outputs a signal proportional to the incident irradiance. The horizontal and vertical displacements T_x and T_y are proportional to the normalized quad-cell signals q_x and q_y,

$$q_x = \frac{(B+D)-(A+C)}{A+B+C+D}$$

$$q_y = \frac{(A+B)-(C+D)}{A+B+C+D}, \tag{55}$$

where $A, B, C,$ and D are signals proportional to the irradiances incident in the detector quadrants as labeled in Fig. 4. The quad-cell signals are converted into transverse displacements using a calibration factor, which is empirically determined by plotting measured quad-cell signals as a function of known displacements of a test spot.

   Another method for determining transverse spot displacement uses a focal plane array with many pixels (more than four) to compute the centroid of the incident irradiance, which reduces to the quad-cell calculation for a four-pixel detector array. The horizontal and vertical spot displacements are computed from the centroid definition

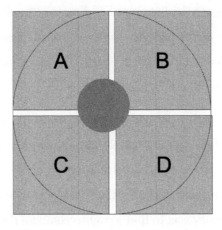

Figure 4:   Quad-cell detector

as

$$T_x = \frac{\iint xI(x_{\mathrm{fp}}, y_{\mathrm{fp}})\mathrm{d}x_{\mathrm{fp}}\mathrm{d}y_{\mathrm{fp}}}{\iint I(x_{\mathrm{fp}}, y_{\mathrm{fp}})\mathrm{d}x_{\mathrm{fp}}\mathrm{d}y_{\mathrm{fp}}}$$

$$T_y = \frac{\iint yI(x_{\mathrm{fp}}, y_{\mathrm{fp}})\mathrm{d}x_{\mathrm{fp}}\mathrm{d}y_{\mathrm{fp}}}{\iint I(x_{\mathrm{fp}}, y_{\mathrm{fp}})\mathrm{d}x_{\mathrm{fp}}\mathrm{d}y_{\mathrm{fp}}},$$

(56)

where $I(x_{\mathrm{fp}}, y_{\mathrm{fp}})$ is the irradiance distribution over the focal plane with coordinates $(x_{\mathrm{fp}}, y_{\mathrm{fp}})$ and the integration is performed over the extent of the detector region subtended by the subaperture.

The wavefront gradient, or slope, obtained from the centroid calculation is actually weighted by the irradiance of the wavefront in the pupil of the Shack-Hartmann sensor. Therefore, another expression often used for Shack-Hartmann slope measurements is the subaperture-averaged intensity-weighted gradient, which is given for the x-gradient of the wavefront incident on the $(m, n)^{\mathrm{th}}$ subaperture by

$$s_{m,n}^x = \frac{\iint I_p(x_p, y_p)\frac{\partial}{\partial x_p}W(x_p, y_p)\mathrm{d}x_p\mathrm{d}y_p}{\iint I_p(x_p, y_p)},$$

(57)

where $W(x_p, y_p)$ is the OPD of the wavefront across the pupil, $I_p(x_p, y_p)$ is the irradiance in the pupil, (x_p, y_p) are the horizontal and vertical pupil coordinates of a given lenslet, and the limits are performed over the extent of the lenslet [62]. Equation (57) is useful for performing fast simulations of Shack-Hartmann slope measurements that include effects of irradiance fluctuations.

There may be better ways of computing subaperture spot displacement than from the centroid algorithm. Some possible methods are maximum-likelihood estimation, Fourier analysis, and periodic correlation [8, 17, 26, 57, 58]. Each of these approaches is discussed in more detail in the literature review in Ch. III. However, since the purpose of this work was to find a way to combine the SH WFS with an SRI in a hybrid WFS, the centroid method was chosen as a reasonable first metric for performance. Future work can evaluate the impact of other slope-estimation techniques on hybrd-WFS performance since, presumably, any improvements to slope estimation over the centroid method should only improve hybrid-WFS performance.

2.5.3 Dynamic Range. The geometry of the Shack-Hartmann sensor allows diffracted light (side lobes) from adjacent subaperture spots to overlap on the detector array. One way of dealing with this is to place guard bands of dead pixels between subaperture detector regions. However, due to the spread of energy over a potentially large area caused by diffraction, it is still possible for subaperture tilt measurements to be influenced by light from adjacent subapertures. This can cause measurement error and limit the dynamic range of the Shack-Hartmann sensor. The centroid algorithm estimates the displacement of the focused spot from the center of the detector array based on the imbalance of energy incident on the detector. Assuming photon-limited noise, the error of slope measurements is primarily impacted by

1. the size of the incident spot relative to the size of the detector array,

2. the spot displacement relative to the size of the detector array, and

3. the size of the spot relative to the size of the pixels in the detector array.

Winick addressed the last item by computing the Cramer-Rao lower bound (CRLB) for slope measurements, which showed that minimum slope estimation error is achieved for one-dimensional slope estimates when the ratio of pixel size to spot size (characterized by diffraction angle λ/d) is between 1 and 2 [91]. This range ensures the spot is small enough to achieve enough sub-pixel resolution to determine the spot location unambiguously while also accounting for error due to noisy pixel outputs. However, Winick's analysis assumed an infinitely large detector array, which neglects the first two dependencies listed above. He also assumed a Gaussian spot instead of a diffraction-limited spot pattern derived from the size and shape of the subapertures. Irwan and Lane show the limitations of assuming a Gaussian spot distribution in a tilt sensor. When a diffraction-limited spot for a circular or square aperture is used and only Poisson noise is assumed, the variance of tilt measurements derived from centroid measurements increases with detector-array size [41]. The natural solution to this problem is the truncation of the detector array, but this injects error that is both a function of detector size and spot displacement due to the truncation of the spot as it moves away from the center of the detector array [41]. The impact of centroid displacement and detector-array size are closely related to one another since a larger detector allows larger spot displacement without significant spot truncation. The tilt variance due to truncation error is very large at small sizes of the detector array. Therefore, the detector array must not be too small or truncation error will dominate, but it must also not be too large or photon noise becomes excessive. In wavefront sensing for atmospheric AO, prior knowledge of the atmospheric coherence width r_0 provides useful information of the expected amount of atmospheric beam spread, which is useful for choosing appropriately-sized Shack-Hartmann lenslets.

Even in the absence of noise and assuming a Gaussian spot, the centroid error depends on detector-array size and spot displacement. A Gaussian irradiance distribution with spot size σ and spot displacement (in the x-direction) T_x is given by

$$I(x,y) = \exp\left[\frac{-(x - T_x)^2}{2\sigma^2}\right]. \tag{58}$$

Substituting this expression into Eq. (56) and evaluating the integrals over a finite detector array with side length L leads to a specific expression for the centroid calculation

$$C_x = \frac{\frac{2\sigma}{\sqrt{2\pi}} \left(e^{-u^2} - e^{-v^2} \right) + T_x \left[\mathrm{erf}(u) + \mathrm{erf}(v) \right]}{\mathrm{erf}(u) + \mathrm{erf}(v)}. \tag{59}$$

The arguments u and v are functions of the detector-array side length L, the spot size σ, and the spot displacement T_x and are given by

$$u = \frac{\sqrt{2(L + 2T_x)}}{4\sigma}, \tag{60}$$

$$v = \frac{\sqrt{2(L - 2T_x)}}{4\sigma}.$$

The error function $\mathrm{erf}(\xi)$ is the result of integrating a Gaussian function and is defined as

$$\mathrm{erf}(\xi) \triangleq \frac{2}{\sqrt{\pi}} \int_0^{\xi} e^{-t^2} \mathrm{d}t.$$

Evaluating Eq. (59) numerically over a range of spot displacements and spot sizes relative to the size of the detector array illustrates the dependence of centroid error on these sensor specifications. Figure 5 shows the resulting error for a detector array with the spot size σ set to a fixed multiple of the pixel size δ_{pix}. The metric plotted in Fig. 5 is normalized centroid error ϵ_C, which was was computed by

$$\epsilon_C = \frac{T_x - C_x}{T_x}. \tag{61}$$

White regions in Fig. 5 correspond to low error, dark regions correspond to high error, and contour lines show the 1%, 4%, 8%, and 12% error levels. This illustrates the effect of a finite detector array on the dynamic range of the centroid algorithm, since the dynamic range should be limited to the region where the centroid error is tolerably low. The error is less than one percent over a fairly large range of detector-array sizes and spot displacements but increases rapidly for values outside this range. The error calculation did not apply the absolute value function, so Fig. 5 also illustrates that

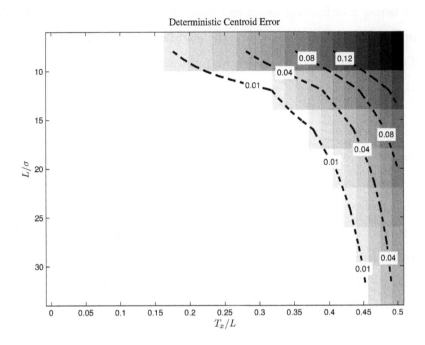

Figure 5:   Truncation error of centroid.

the centroid calculation is always less than the actual spot displacement, *i.e* it is biased towards the center of the subaperture. Furthermore, the figure illustrates that centroid error is a nonlinear function of both L/σ and T_x/L. Because of this limitation on dynamic range, even in the absence of noise, spot-displacement sensors based on the centroid calculation require calibration for a given lens and detector array.

2.5.4   Noise-Induced Centroid Error.   A model for centroid error due to photon noise and scintillation is presented in Ch. IV. While this model could be adapted to account for truncation error in a Monte Carlo study, it is primarily intended for evaluating the impact of noise on centroid error. However, previously published work in this area provides guidelines for choosing pixel size and detector-array size, which can then be evaluated for noise-induced error using the model presented in Ch. IV. In the present work, SH subapertures lengths were chosen to be less than or equal to r_0, and the lenslet focal lengths and detector arrays were designed to achieve two pixels across a diffraction angle and eight pixels across a subaperture. These design parameters were chosen based on the guidelines presented in [41] and [91] and appeared to maintain a good balance between the competing requirements of dynamic range (*a.k.a.* truncation error) and photon-noise-induced error.

    2.5.5 Impact of Irradiance Fluctuations. Reflection of a coherent wave from objects with random surface roughness or accumulation of phase disturbances over long propagation distances through strong turbulence causes random fluctuations in the amplitude of the propagating optical field. These amplitude fluctuations result in a random distribution of bright and dark regions in the detected irradiance patterns. Irradiance fluctuations due to random surface roughness are generally called *speckle*, while those due to atmospheric propagation are referred to as *scintillation*. Irradiance fluctuations can degrade wavefront estimates. This is especially true for least-squares-reconstructed wavefronts from slope measurements. Because the slopes are equivalent to the subaperture-averaged intensity-weighted phase gradients [Eq. (57)], their error is inversely proportional to the irradiance. If a subaperture of a Shack-Hartmann sensor samples a region of the field with a small amplitude, the spot irradiance can fall below the noise level and cause a zero-slope measurement even when the phase gradient over that region of the field is non-zero. This issue motivates improvements in the SNR of Shack-Hartmann sensors designed to operate in strong atmospheric turbulence. However, SNR often competes with the requirement that the subapertures are small enough to partition the incident wavefront into samples that are well-approximated by plane waves. Also, even in the complete absence of noise, the complex field of the incident wavefront could be identically zero in a region of non-zero phase gradient, which would result in least-squares-reconstruction errors for a Shack-Hartmann sensor. Much of the interest in exploring alternatives to the Shack-Hartmann WFS for AO is motivated by simulation studies that have shown the rapid degradation of SH-WFS performance with increasing scintillation strength, especially when the wavefront is insufficiently sampled [3]. This may be an area where combining the Shack-Hartmann sensor with a second sensor such as the SRI may prove helpful. Toward this end, the shot-noise-induced centroid-error model presented in Ch. IV was developed that accounts for the effect of random fluctuations of the classical irradiance.

2.6 The Self-Referencing Interferometer

The self-referencing interferometer exploits recent advances in fiber optics and camera technology to implement a phase-shifting point-diffraction interferometer (PDI), which can estimate the phase of the incident wavefront from the recorded irradiance patterns (*i.e.* interferograms) of two interfered optical fields. This section summarizes interferometric theory, presents one method of implementing phase-shifting interferometry, and describes the concept and operation of the SRI as a wavefront sensor.

2.6.1 Theory of Interference. The spatially distributed irradiance $I(\boldsymbol{r})$ of a single polarization component of an EM wave is represented by a time- and space-varying complex electric field $E(\boldsymbol{r}, t)$ averaged over some finite period of time, *i.e.*

$$I(\boldsymbol{r}) = \left\langle |E(\boldsymbol{r}, t)|^2 \right\rangle_T, \tag{62}$$

where $\boldsymbol{r}$ is a spatial coordinate vector and $\langle g \rangle_T$ indicates the time average of g over the time interval T. The temporal and spatial variations of two EM waves with the same angular frequency ω can be written as [14]

$$
\begin{aligned}
E_1(\boldsymbol{r}, t) &= \Re\left\{ U_1(\boldsymbol{r})e^{-\mathrm{j}\omega t} \right\} \\
E_2(\boldsymbol{r}, t) &= \Re\left\{ U_2(\boldsymbol{r})e^{-\mathrm{j}\omega t} \right\},
\end{aligned}
\tag{63}
$$

where t is a temporal coordinate, and $\Re\{u\}$ is an operator that returns the real part of the complex number u. The spatially-dependent complex-field amplitudes $U_1(\boldsymbol{r})$

and $U_2(\boldsymbol{r})$ are defined as

$$
\begin{aligned}
U_1(\boldsymbol{r}) &= |U_1(\boldsymbol{r})|e^{j\phi_1(\boldsymbol{r})} \\
U_2(\boldsymbol{r}) &= |U_2(\boldsymbol{r})|e^{j\phi_2(\boldsymbol{r})},
\end{aligned}
\tag{64}
$$

where $\phi_i(\boldsymbol{r})$ is the spatially-varying phase of the time-independent complex field $U_i(\boldsymbol{r})$ with phasor amplitude given by $|U_i(\boldsymbol{r})|$; $i \in \{1,2\}$. Interference of parallel polarization components of two electric fields E_1 and E_2 is represented as the sum of the two fields

$$
E = E_1 + E_2,
\tag{65}
$$

where the explicit dependence on $\boldsymbol{r}$ and t has been temporarily dropped to simplify the notation in the next step. Using Eq. (62) on the two summed fields yields an expression for the irradiance due to the interference of two fields

$$
\begin{aligned}
I &= \left\langle |E_1 + E_2|^2 \right\rangle_T \\
&= \left\langle E_1 E_1^* \right\rangle_T + \left\langle E_2 E_2^* \right\rangle_T + 2 \left\langle E_1 E_2^* \right\rangle_T \\
&= I_1 + I_2 + 2I_{1,2}.
\end{aligned}
\tag{66}
$$

The superscript asterisk * in Eq. (66) indicates complex conjugation, the terms I_1 and I_2 are the irradiances due to each individual field acting alone, and $I_{1,2}$ is a cross term that gives information about the relationship between the two fields. For two time-averaged fields interfering in a plane perpendicular to the z-axis, the irradiance cross term can be expressed as

$$
I_{1,2}(x,y) = |U_1(x,y)||U_2(x,y)|\Re\left\{ e^{j[\phi_1(x,y)-\phi_2(x,y)]} \right\}.
\tag{67}
$$

Defining $\Delta\phi(x,y) = \phi_1(x,y) - \phi_2(x,y)$ and applying Euler's identity to extract the real part of the complex exponential term, the cross term becomes

$$I_{1,2}(x,y) = \sqrt{I_1(x,y)I_2(x,y)}\cos[\Delta\phi(x,y)], \qquad (68)$$

where the individual scalar-field amplitudes have been expressed as the square root of their irradiance values. In the special case where $I_1(x,y) = I_2(x,y)$, using the definition for $I_{1,2}(\boldsymbol{r})$ from Eq. (68) in Eq. (66) leads to the following expression for the interferogram irradiance [14]:

$$I(x,y) = 2I_1(x,y)\left\{1 + \cos[\Delta\phi(x,y)]\right\}. \qquad (69)$$

Although the preceding was based on the assumption of parallel polarization between the interfering fields, these expressions also apply to randomly-polarized waves and elliptically-polarized waves [14]. However, Fresnel and Arago showed that waves with orthogonal linear polarization do not interfere, so Eq. (69) does not apply in that case [14]. Regardless, Eq. (69) shows that it is possible to examine the irradiance pattern caused by two coherent EM fields interfered with one another to estimate the spatially-distributed phase differences between them. Interferometry generally involves adding a field with a known wavefront, usually called the reference, to a field with an unknown wavefront and then using the resulting interferograms to estimate the phase of the unknown wavefront.

2.6.2 *Fringe Visibility and Coherence.* Fringe visibility $\mathcal{V}$ is the depth of the variations in irradiance across an interferogram and was first defined by Michelson as

$$\mathcal{V} = \frac{I_{max} - I_{min}}{I_{max} + I_{min}}, \qquad (70)$$

where I_{max} and I_{min} are the maximum and minimum values of irradiance in the interferogram [38]. A very useful expression for fringe visibility defines it as a function of the individual irradiances I_1 and I_2 of the interfered fields and the degree of coherence $|\gamma_{12}(\tau)|$ and is given by

$$\mathcal{V} = \frac{2\sqrt{I_1 I_2}}{I_1 + I_2}|\gamma_{12}(\tau)|. \tag{71}$$

According to Eq. (71), $\mathcal{V} = 0$ for the incoherent case and increases with the degree of coherence achieving a maximum when the interfered fields are completely coherent. Interferometric WFS's must maintain a high degree of temporal coherence between the reference and signal legs of the interferometer. This implies that the beacon for an interferometric WFS must have a long coherence time Δt_c, which is equivalent to saying that the beacon must have a narrow optical bandwidth $\Delta \nu$ since $\Delta t_c \approx 1/\Delta \nu$ [38]. Therefore, AO systems that rely on an interferometric WFS must generally have some type of artificial beacon such as a laser guide star or the beam from a free-space optical-communications channel. Interferometric WFS's are further limited by the finite spatial extent of the beacon through the dependence of fringe visibility on spatial coherence. If the beacon is a perfect point source, spatial coherence is not an issue since $|\gamma_{12}(0)| = 1$. However, beacons with finite spatial extent experience decreased spatial coherence and therefore degrade fringe visibility and the quality of interferometric wavefront estimates. Equation (71) also shows the dependence of fringe visibility on the balance of energy between the two interfered fields. This can be made more clear by letting $I_1 = I$ and $I_2 = aI$ in Eq. (71), where $a \triangleq I_2/I_1$, in which case

$$\mathcal{V} \propto \frac{2\sqrt{a}}{a + 1}. \tag{72}$$

This expression shows that visibility is degraded by energy imbalance between the two legs of the interferometer even if there is perfect coherence. Visibility versus I_2/I_1 is plotted in Fig. 6, which shows that the visibility peaks when $I_1 = I_2$, although there is a relatively wide range of values of $0.5 \le a \le 2$ over which $\mathcal{V} > 0.9$. However, larger imbalances between I_1 and I_2 can reduce the fringe visibility significantly.

2.6.3 Phase-Shifting Interferometry. Phase-shifting interferometry provides a means of measuring modulo-2π phase differences $\Delta\phi(x, y)$ dynamically. Using the

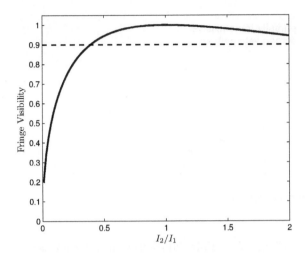

Figure 6:   Fringe visibility and energy imbalance

expression for the interferogram cross term given in Eq. (68), Eq. (66) can be rewritten as

$$I(x,y) = A + B \cos[\Delta\phi(x,y) + \theta], \tag{73}$$

where $A = I_1(x,y) + I_2(x,y)$ and $B = [I_1(x,y)I_2(x,y)]^{1/2}$ have been defined to simplify the analysis, and θ represents a phase shift introduced into the reference beam. Multiple phase shifts are required and can be introduced either successively in time to the whole reference beam or simultaneously to spatially-separated replicas of the reference beam. In a common approach called the four-bin phase-shifting algorithm, the reference beam is shifted by $\theta = 0, \pi/2, \pi$, and $3\pi/2$ [45, 63]. The resulting interferograms have the following trigonometric forms:

$$
\begin{aligned}
I_1(x,y) &= A + B\cos[\Delta\phi(x,y)] \\
I_2(x,y) &= A + B\cos[\Delta\phi(x,y) + \pi/2] &= A - B\sin[\Delta\phi(x,y)] \\
I_3(x,y) &= A + B\cos[\Delta\phi(x,y) + \pi] &= A - B\cos[\Delta\phi(x,y)] \\
I_4(x,y) &= A + B\cos[\Delta\phi(x,y) + 3\pi/2] &= A + B\sin[\Delta\phi(x,y)].
\end{aligned}
\tag{74}
$$

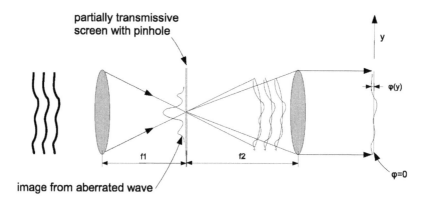

Figure 7:   Point-diffraction interferometer.

Subtracting $I_2(x, y)$ from $I_4(x, y)$ results in $2B\sin[\Delta\phi(x, y)]$ and subtracting $I_3(x, y)$ from $I_1(x, y)$ results in $2B\cos[\Delta\phi(x, y)]$ so that

$$\frac{I_4(x, y) - I_2(x, y)}{I_1(x, y) - I_3(x, y)} = \tan[\Delta\phi(x, y)]. \tag{75}$$

Therefore, the spatially-varying phase difference between the two legs of the interferometer can be computed from

$$\Delta\phi(x, y) = \text{Tan}^{-1}\left[\frac{I_4(x, y) - I_2(x, y)}{I_1(x, y) - I_3(x, y)}\right]. \tag{76}$$

The capitalized inverse-tangent-function notation in Eq. (76) indicates use of the four-quadrant inverse-tangent algorithm, which tracks the signs of the numerator and denominator of the argument to compute the principal values in the interval $[-\pi, \pi)$.

2.6.4 Self Referencing Interferometer.   The SRI is a special type of PDI that interferes an aberrated wavefront with a plane wave obtained by spatially filtering a sample of the aberrated beam. Figure 7 illustrates the concept of a PDI. A lens with focal length f_1 focuses the incoming wavefront, which passes through a partially transmissive screen with a pinhole placed a distance f_1 behind the lens. The pinhole

50

spatially filters the part of the aberrated beam that passes through it, which ideally creates a point source with a diverging spherical wavefront that is superposed with the aberrated wavefront partially transmitted by the screen. A second lens, located a distance equal to its focal length f_2 after the screen, recollimates both wavefronts, which interfere with one another at a photodetector, creating an interferogram. The phase differences $\Delta\phi(x, y)$ between the two wavefronts can be extracted using Eq. (69) or Eq. (76) and phase-shifting techniques. One immediately-apparent concern with this approach is the adverse impact on the fringe visibility due to the inherent energy imbalance between the aberrated beam and the plane-wave reference. As discussed in Sec. 2.6.2, even with perfect coherence, the fringe visibility suffers when there is a large imbalance between the two interfered wavefronts.

The SRI overcomes the decreased fringe visibility of the PDI by coupling a sampled portion of the aberrated wavefront into a single-mode fiber, which provides the spatial filtering. The SRI is illustrated in Fig. 8. In this approach, the energy balance between the two legs can be better managed by choosing the appropriate ratio for the beam splitter. Early SRI work assumed amplification of the reference through stimulated emission in the fiber would be necessary to achieve adequate visibility, but noise analysis showed that amplification with commercially available optical amplifiers actually degraded SRI performance [64]. However, if the noise characteristics of optical amplifiers improve sufficiently, this may again become an area of research for improving SRI performance. Although the SRI provides improved fringe visibility compared to a PDI, visibility can still be a significant issue for the SRI prior to closing the AO loop. Visibility is decreased when very little light is available to the reference because of poor fiber-coupling efficiency caused by the severely aberrated input beam. This is yet another reason a hybrid WFS using both a SH WFS and an SRI has been suggested, since the SH WFS may prove useful in initially closing the AO loop when the SRI's fiber-coupling efficiency drops too low.

The fiber-coupled reference beam also provides a means of implementing time-stepped phase shifting where the phase delays are implemented inside the fiber. For

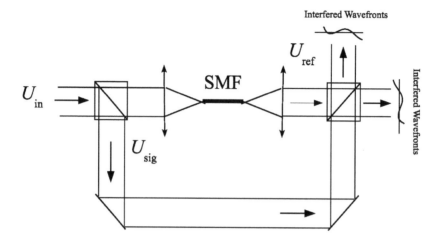

Figure 8:   Self-Referencing Interferometer.

instance, temporal phase shifting might be implemented by stretching the fiber to different lengths corresponding to the desired OPD and holding it at each length long enough to capture images of the interferograms. Alternatively, spatial phase-shifting techniques use stationary optics to split the reference and signal beams and redirect them to interfere in separate 'bins' at the photodetector array. Spatial phase-shifting architectures introduce additional hardware complexity and require additional splitting of available light, but these costs tend to be outweighed by advantages gained such as insensitivity to temporal atmospheric changes, more stable phase-shifting, and a much improved ability to tolerate platform vibration [63].

The SRI's single-mode fiber (SMF) spatially filters the incident wavefront, ideally allowing only the lowest-order Gaussian mode of the input to pass through to the reference leg. After collimation, the reference is essentially a uniform plane wave and is assumed to have constant, zero phase across the exit pupil. Therefore, the phase-shifting equations are simplified by recognizing that $\Delta\phi(x, y) = \phi_1(x, y)$, so the SRI measurements are directly modulated by the spatially-varying phase of the aberrated wavefront.

Because the four-quadrant, inverse-tangent operator is limited to phase values between $-\pi$ and π, the SRI phase measurements are modulo-2π, or wrapped. Therefore, SRI phase measurements must be unwrapped before commanding a continuous-facesheet DM because such a DM cannot apply the sharp 2π discontinuities in the wrapped phase [63]. However, SRI measurements could directly drive a segmented piston-only DM or LC SLM. Nearly all phase-unwrapping techniques involve wrapping the gradients computed from the wrapped phase and then integrating over some path [33]. Since the first step in unwrapping is computation of the phase gradient, this problem is identical to the phase reconstruction required for a gradient-sensing WFS such as the Shack-Hartmann sensor. Therefore, the SRI WFS still requires computationally expensive algorithms and parallel processing to unwrap phase estimates in real time. However, unlike gradient sensors, the SRI produces measurements that are mathematically formulated as a linear combination of the complex field with statistics that are defined by the coherence factor [6]. Because the coherence factor is independent of the scintillation index, so are the statistics of the mathematical formulation of SRI measurements (*i.e.* formulation error). This predicts that SRI measurements should be immune to scintillation and is therefore better suited to strong-turbulence applications [3]. However, SRI sensitivity to scintillation has been observed in laboratory experiments using an SRI [18]. The model for SRI phase error presented in Ch. V shows a weak dependence of SRI measurements on scintillation due to the coupled effects of random intensity fluctuations and photon noise.

Besides the need for phase unwrapping when driving a continuous-facesheet DM, there are a few other issues unique to the SRI WFS. Because the SRI is an interferometer, the optical paths between the beacon and reference must be carefully matched to maintain the required temporal coherence between the reference and the signal wavefront, especially if the reference is amplified through stimulated emission. Maintaining common path lengths in an SRI that uses spatial phase shifting is important, since this approach creates four separate paths that must be matched. However, temporal phase shifting provides its own challenges, especially since AO systems are generally used to correct for dynamic phase aberrations. The required temporal coherence also limits the SRI to monochromatic wavefronts, which limits their applicability to AO systems that use artificial beacons. Furthermore, because the SRI averages the field over each subaperture, large tilts can be poorly sensed. This phenomenon is considered to be responsible for the fact that certain types of reconstructed gradient measurements outperform the SRI in weak turbulence when the subaperture side length d is larger than the atmospheric coherence width r_0 [63]. Also, when phase measurements are controlling a DM in an AO system with only one subaperture per actuator, the SRI may not sense attempted DM corrections at points in the spatial field with zero amplitude (branch points), which can lead to a build-up of phase on actuators corresponding to branch-point locations [63]. The hybrid WFS presented in Ch. VI was designed to improve SRI performance as much as possible by mitigating the impact of these issues through good SRI design and by including a SH WFS.

2.7 Estimation Theory

Photo-detection involves the interaction of light with matter, which is a process with inherent uncertainty that can be treated as a type of noise. Generation of electrical signals from detected photons can inject additional noise, and reading the electrical signals from a photodetector causes even more noise. Because light detection is an inherently noisy process, any sensor relying on it must estimate the best-possible value of some quantity from noisy measurements. Therefore, statistical decision making and estimation theory play an important role in wavefront-sensor design. This section closely follows the description of statistical decision theory presented by Barrett and Myers [7]. The block diagram for their model of statistical decision making based on the output of an imaging system is shown in Fig. 9. A wavefront estimator fits into this model as the observer because it uses images to make decisions about the incident wavefront. A wavefront sensor includes both the imaging hardware and the observer. The observer performs one of two types of statistical inference when

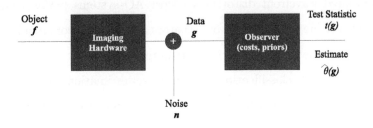

Figure 9:   Decision-making process for an imaging system

making decisions based on the output of the imaging system, *classification* or *parameter estimation*. *Classification* occurs any time there is a finite number of possible outcomes and is used in pattern recognition, signal detection, differential diagnosis, and hypothesis testing. *Parameter estimation* can be regarded as the limit of hypothesis testing as the number of hypotheses becomes infinite; then the task is estimation of one or more numerical parameters based on the data. If the observer seeks to classify the object based on the data, then the observer's task is classification. For example, if the object is an orange, then the data might include things like shape, color, and size. Obviously, classification presumes a great deal of *a priori* information about the object, which must be built up from empirical observations of parameters used to describe the object. If the observer seeks to determine the size of an orange by measuring it, then the observer's task is parameter estimation, and the size is a parameter that may be composed of data such as the circumferences of orthogonal cross sections of the orange.

A WFS in an AO system may perform either or both of these two statistical-inference tasks. If an AO system uses a DM with a small number of actuators that can only accept commands from a finite, discrete set, then the WFS's job is to determine which combination of DM commands (i.e. which DM mode) provides the best wavefront correction, which is a classification task. For a large number of actuators and/or many possible command values at each actuator, the problem becomes one of parameter estimation where the parameters are the actuator commands that best correct the unwanted wavefront distortions. Most AO systems perform parameter estimation because of the large number of actuators and possible commands involved. However, some phase-unwrapping algorithms require branch-point detection, which is a classification task. While classification and parameter estimation are closely related, the work proposed here is primarily concerned with parameter estimation. Therefore the theory relevant to classification tasks (*a.k.a.* detection theory) is omitted to focus on the more immediately-relevant task of parameter estimation.

2.7.1 The Decision-Making Process. Statistical decision making assumes randomness in the information used to make decisions. When it is impossible or impractical to know every cause for some observation, then statistics for the observation become very useful. Classifying some variables as random inputs to a process helps to simplify predictive models based on deterministic analysis. In fact, deterministic models generally require assumptions of ideal conditions and attribute deviations from predicted outcomes to the impact of random inputs or noise. Noise defined in this way is present in every physical process, and models based on sound deterministic analysis can be optimized for real-world conditions by including the impact of noise in the decision-making process.

The model shown in Fig. 9 assumes the imaging hardware performs functions that can be explained with a purely deterministic transfer function (or mapping operator) $\mathcal{H}$. The data vector g results from this transfer function operating on the object vector f with deviations from the ideal predictions modeled as a noise vector n. The mathematical expression for this process is

$$g = \mathcal{H}f + n, \tag{77}$$

which comes directly from the definition of noise as the random deviations from the deterministic predictions of $\mathcal{H}$. The quality of decisions is fundamentally limited by the fidelity of the deterministic model. However, without properly accounting for

56

random inputs, it is impossible to measure how well the deterministic model predicts outcomes.

2.7.2 Likelihood Functions. Statistical inference about a random process requires a model for the conditional probability density function (pdf) on the data. In detection and estimation theory, these conditional pdf's are called likelihood functions because they express the likelihood of obtaining the data g from the object f or from some numerical parameter θ that describes the object. The likelihood function $p(g|f)$ simply describes the probability of obtaining the data g given the object f. The likelihood that a set of data represents some parameter θ is described by the likelihood function $p(g|\theta)$.

2.7.3 Cost and Risk Functions. Optimal estimation involves minimizing the cost or risk associated with incorrectly assigning an estimate $\hat{\theta}$ to the parameter θ. A cost function $C(\hat{\theta}, \theta)$ quantifies this cost. A common cost function is the square of the distance between the parameter and the estimate,

$$C(\hat{\theta}, \theta) = (\hat{\theta} - \theta)^2. \tag{78}$$

Risk is defined as the average cost function and can be quantified in one of three ways depending on the averaging operation(s) chosen. These three definitions are

$$\bar{C}(\theta) = \left\langle C(\hat{\theta}, \theta) \right\rangle_{g|\theta} \tag{79}$$

$$\bar{C}(g) = \left\langle C(\hat{\theta}, \theta) \right\rangle_{\theta|g} \tag{80}$$

$$\bar{C} = \left\langle \bar{C}(\theta) \right\rangle_{\theta} = \left\langle \bar{C}(g) \right\rangle_{g}, \tag{81}$$

where angle brackets indicate an ensemble average or expected value, and the subscripts on the angle brackets indicate which pdf is involved in the averaging process. Equation (79) performs the average over many realizations of data for each value of the parameter to define risk as a function of θ. Barrett and Myers identify this type

57

of risk as indicating a frequentist approach. Equation (80) evaluates the expectation using the posterior pdf on $\boldsymbol{\theta}$ for a given data vector to define the risk as a function of $\boldsymbol{g}$, which is a Bayesian-purist approach. Equation (81) gives the *Bayes risk*, which either averages $\bar{C}(\boldsymbol{\theta})$ over an assumed distribution for the values of $\boldsymbol{\theta}$ or averages $\bar{C}(\boldsymbol{g})$ over an ensemble of possible data vectors. The Bayes risk summarizes the overall performance of the estimator in the presence of both measurement noise and object randomness.

2.7.4 Bias, Variance, and Mean Square Error.   Bias is a measure of the closeness of the average value of an estimate $\bar{\hat{\theta}}$ to the true value of the underlying parameter θ and is given by

$$b = \bar{\hat{\theta}} - \theta. \tag{82}$$

The average value of the estimate is also called the conditional mean since it is calculated from the pdf of the data conditioned on a particular value of θ, *i.e.* the conditional mean of an estimate is given by

$$\bar{\hat{\theta}} = \int p(\boldsymbol{g}|\theta)\hat{\theta}(\boldsymbol{g})\mathrm{d}\boldsymbol{g}, \tag{83}$$

where the integral is performed over all elements of the data vector $\boldsymbol{g}$. An estimate with a conditional mean equal to the true value of the parameter is said to be unbiased. Barrett and Myers define the *estimability* of a parameter based on the existence of an unbiased estimator for all true values of the underlying parameter for some set of data. Bias often indicates the existence of an error in the estimation model or incorrect assumptions about the likelihood function used to compute the conditional mean. In approaches that use the likelihood function to form parameter estimates, bias due to incorrect assumptions about $p(\boldsymbol{g}|\theta)$ may go undetected leading to incorrect assumptions about the bias of the estimator or even the estimability of the parameter. If the pdf of the parameter is known, then the average bias $\bar{b}$ can be defined in terms of the conditional mean and the true value of the parameter, both averaged over all possible values of the parameter, *i.e.*

$$\bar{b} = \int p(\theta)\bar{\hat{\theta}}\mathrm{d}\theta - \int p(\theta)\theta\mathrm{d}\theta. \tag{84}$$

This may result in an average unbiased estimate, which could be used to characterize a parameter as estimable even if the estimate is biased for some values of the parameter.

While bias is important because it gives a sense of the fidelity of the estimation model, another important characteristic of an estimate is its ability to reproduce nearly the same value every time it is applied to a given parameter. Two important metrics that provide a measure of this characteristic are the variance and the mean square error (MSE). Variance gives a measure of the variability of estimates around the conditional mean,

$$\mathrm{Var}(\hat{\theta}) = \left\langle \left| \hat{\theta} - \bar{\hat{\theta}} \right|^2 \right\rangle_{g|\theta}. \tag{85}$$

MSE gives a measure of the variability of estimates around the true value,

$$\mathrm{MSE}(\theta) = \left\langle \left| \hat{\theta} - \theta \right|^2 \right\rangle_{g|\theta}. \tag{86}$$

The variance and the MSE are the same when the estimate is unbiased. The ultimate goals in parameter estimation are eliminating bias and minimizing variance, since this essentially amounts to estimating the true value of the parameter correctly and confidently from relatively small numbers of samples. This work employs the maximum-likelihood approach to combining two WFS's, which minimizes the variance and produces an unbiased estimator (see Sec. 2.7.5).

The bias of Eq. (82) is easily generalized to a vector bias $\boldsymbol{b}$ by simply replacing the scalar quantities $\bar{\hat{\theta}}$ and θ with vector quantities $\bar{\hat{\boldsymbol{\theta}}}$ and $\boldsymbol{\theta}$. A full characterization of the variance of a vector random variable requires computation of the covariance matrix

$$\mathbf{K}_{\hat{\boldsymbol{\theta}}} = \left\langle \left(\hat{\boldsymbol{\theta}} - \bar{\hat{\boldsymbol{\theta}}} \right) \left(\hat{\boldsymbol{\theta}} - \bar{\hat{\boldsymbol{\theta}}} \right)^{\dagger} \right\rangle = \left\langle \Delta\hat{\boldsymbol{\theta}}\Delta\hat{\boldsymbol{\theta}}^{\dagger} \right\rangle, \tag{87}$$

where the † superscript indicates the combined conjugate and transpose operations. The diagonals of $\mathbf{K}_{\hat{\theta}}$ are the variances of the components of $\hat{\theta}$, and the MSE can be written as

$$\text{MSE} = \text{tr}\left[\mathbf{K}_{\hat{\theta}}\right] + \text{tr}\left[\boldsymbol{b}\boldsymbol{b}^{\dagger}\right], \tag{88}$$

where $\text{tr}[\mathbf{M}]$ is the sum of the diagonal elements (the trace) of the matrix $\mathbf{M}$.

2.7.5 Maximum-Likelihood Estimation. Maximum-likelihood estimation was used in this work to optimally combine two WFS's into a hybrid WFS. The maximum-likelihood estimate (MLE) is the value of the parameter θ that maximizes the likelihood function, or equivalently, the log-likelihood function $\ln[p(\boldsymbol{g}|\boldsymbol{\theta})]$, i.e.

$$\hat{\theta}_{\text{ML}} \triangleq \max_{\theta}\left\{\ln[p(\boldsymbol{g}|\boldsymbol{\theta})]\right\}. \tag{89}$$

The score $\boldsymbol{s}$ describes the sensitivity of the likelihood to changes in parameters and is given by

$$\boldsymbol{s} = \frac{\frac{\partial}{\partial\boldsymbol{\theta}}p(\boldsymbol{g}|\boldsymbol{\theta})}{p(\boldsymbol{g}|\boldsymbol{\theta})} = \frac{\partial}{\partial\boldsymbol{\theta}}\ln[p(\boldsymbol{g}|\boldsymbol{\theta})]. \tag{90}$$

When averaged over the data for a given $\boldsymbol{\theta}$, $\boldsymbol{s}$ is a zero-mean random vector. The MLE is generally computed by setting $\boldsymbol{s}(\boldsymbol{g}, \boldsymbol{\theta}) = 0$ and solving for $\boldsymbol{\theta}$. The covariance matrix of the score is called the Fisher information matrix,

$$\mathbf{F} = \left\langle \boldsymbol{s}\boldsymbol{s}^{\top} \right\rangle_{g|\theta}. \tag{91}$$

Barrett and Myers present an interesting proof based primarily on properties of positive-semidefinite matrices that

$$\mathbf{K}_{\epsilon} \geq \mathbf{F}^{-1}, \tag{92}$$

with matrix inequality defined according to the Loewner ordering convention (Appendix A of [7]). Evaluating this inequality at only the diagonal elements of $\mathbf{K}_{\epsilon}$ and $\mathbf{F}$ formed by defining the random variable as the estimation error $\boldsymbol{\epsilon} = \hat{\boldsymbol{\theta}} - \boldsymbol{\theta}$ for an unbiased estimate results in the following expression for the Cramer-Rao lower bound (CRLB):

$$[\mathbf{K}_\epsilon]_{nn} = \text{Var}(\hat{\theta} - \theta) \geq [\mathbf{F}^{-1}]_{nn}. \tag{93}$$

This gives a lower bound for the variance of the estimation error. The CRLB is derived in standard texts on estimation theory; some use the estimation error as the random variable [84], while others use the estimate itself [55]. For an unbiased estimator of a scalar parameter, the CRLB applied to the estimation error reduces to

$$\text{Var}(\hat{\theta} - \theta) \geq \frac{1}{\left\langle \left[\frac{\partial}{\partial \theta} \ln[p(\boldsymbol{g}|\theta)]\right]^2 \right\rangle}. \tag{94}$$

For an estimator with bias $\boldsymbol{b}$, the inequality of Eq. (92) becomes

$$\mathbf{K}_\epsilon \geq (\nabla_{\boldsymbol{\theta}} \boldsymbol{b} + \mathbf{I}) \, \mathbf{F}^{-1} \, (\nabla_{\boldsymbol{\theta}} \boldsymbol{b} + \mathbf{I})^\top, \tag{95}$$

where $\nabla_{\boldsymbol{\theta}}$ indicates the gradient operator with respect to the components of the vector parameter $\boldsymbol{\theta}$. Therefore, a biased estimator of a scalar parameter has a lower bound on the variance of the estimation error given by

$$\text{Var}\{\hat{\theta} - \theta\} \geq \frac{\left(\frac{\mathrm{d}}{\mathrm{d}\theta}b(\theta) + 1\right)^2}{\left\langle \left[\frac{\partial}{\partial \theta} \ln[p(\boldsymbol{g}|\theta)]\right]^2 \right\rangle}. \tag{96}$$

This form of the CRLB shows the impact of bias on the variance of an estimator. If the bias is constant, then $db(\theta)/d\theta = 0$, and the variance is unaffected by the bias. This type of bias is often called a *known bias*, and an unbiased estimator can always be obtained from it simply by subtracting off the bias [84]. If the bias is a function of the value of the parameter, the estimate has an *unknown* bias, and the lower bound on the variance of the estimate depends on how much b varies with θ [7, 84].

The CRLB holds for any rule for estimating $\boldsymbol{\theta}$. An *efficient* estimator is one that attains the equality in Eq. (93), and if an efficient estimator for a parameter exists, the

MLE of that parameter is efficient. Also, the MLE is consistent, which means that it converges to the correct value of $\boldsymbol{\theta}$ as the number of samples approaches infinity. The MLE is also asymptotically efficient, which means that it achieves the equality of the CRLB as the number of samples approaches infinity. Finally, as the number of samples approaches infinity, the distribution of samples of the MLE is Gaussian. The MLE also has the property of invariance, which means that the MLE for a function of an estimated parameter is the function of the MLE for that parameter. These properties are well-documented in texts on estimation theory and make the MLE a very powerful method of estimating an unknown parameter, which either is deterministic or has an unknown random distribution, from random data [7, 55, 84].

The process of finding the MLE for a parameter from data with a known, or at-least well-characterized, likelihood function is very straight forward. In many cases, it is simply a matter of setting the score (i.e. the gradient of the log-likelihood equation) equal to zero and solving for θ. If this cannot be accomplished analytically, it is often approached numerically through some type of iterative search of the parameter space, and modern numerical methods offer several methods for quickly converging to the MLE in such an approach.

2.8   Phase Unwrapping and Reconstruction

An ideal AO system would measure and correct the atmospheric amplitude and phase perturbations of the complex field of an incident EM wave. Practical AO systems generally act only on the phase of the optical field since amplification of the amplitude injects noise, and attenuation discards precious signal power. Phase estimation tends to be far more important in most cases anyway because the field amplitude often does not vary significantly over the WFS pupil, and pupil phase has a greater impact on imaging quality [33]. Therefore, the WFS's main job is phase estimation. The SH WFS's phase estimates must be reconstructed from slope measurements, and the SRI phase estimates must be unwrapped to control a continuous-facesheet DM. Phase unwrapping and reconstruction are similar processes that can complicate wave-

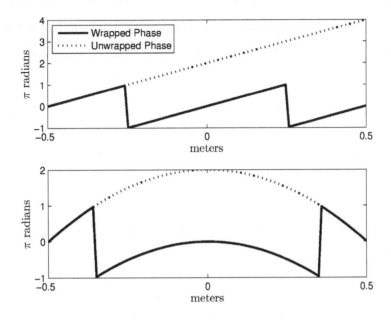

Figure 10:   Wrapped and unwrapped phase

front sensing. This section outlines the basic theory and discusses the issues involved
in phase unwrapping and reconstruction for optical fields.

2.8.1   Phase Unwrapping.   Optical phase is *defined* as the inverse tangent
of the ratio of the imaginary and real parts of a complex optical field. The inverse-
tangent function has principal values restricted to the interval $[-\pi/2, \pi/2]$. Using
the four-quadrant inverse-tangent function, which tracks the signs of the real and
imaginary parts of a complex number, extends the range of the inverse tangent to
the interval $[-\pi, \pi]$. For most applications, modulo-2π, *i.e* wrapped, phase is sufficient. However, optical phase has physically significant meaning that motivates
a need to know its unwrapped value because a continuous-facesheet DM must try
to match the shape of the phase. Wrapped phase causes discontinuities in the DM's
facesheet, which can cause performance degradation if the discontinuities are too large
or poorly placed [53]. Figure 10 illustrates one-dimensional, wrapped and unwrapped
linear phase (top) and quadratic phase (bottom). For a noiseless optical field with

measurable intensity at all points, phase unwrapping simply involves computation of phase differences between adjacent points, wrapping those phase differences modulo-2π, and then integrating along some path. This is sometimes referred to as Itoh's method, which operates on two-dimensional fields by first unwrapping the leftmost column of the phase and then unwrapping each row using the unwrapped value from the first column as the initial value [33]. Review of the source code for MATLAB®'s unwrap function reveals that it uses Itoh's method [47]. Mathematically, this method of phase unwrapping can be stated as a line integral of gradients over a path C given by

$$\phi(\boldsymbol{r}) = \int_C \nabla\phi \cdot \mathbf{d}\boldsymbol{r} + \phi(\boldsymbol{r}_0), \tag{97}$$

where $\nabla\phi$ is the vector field produced by computing the gradient of the phase $\phi(x, y)$, $\boldsymbol{r} = (x, y)$ is a two-dimensional spatial-coordinate vector, and $\phi(\boldsymbol{r}_0)$ is a constant phase value taken to be the phase at some reference point (x_0, y_0).

The unwrapping problem is trivially solved with Itoh's method as long as the result of the integration in Eq. (97) is independent of the path. The following equivalent, necessary, and sufficient conditions for path independence of some directional derivative $\boldsymbol{F}$ are helpful in understanding difficulties that arise in phase unwrapping:

$$\oint \boldsymbol{F} \cdot \mathbf{d}\boldsymbol{r} = 0, \tag{98}$$

and

$$\nabla \times \boldsymbol{F} \equiv \mathbf{0}. \tag{99}$$

The condition in Eq. (98) requires that the integral of $\boldsymbol{F}$ around every simple closed path is zero, while the condition of Eq. (99) says that path independence holds as long as the curl of $\boldsymbol{F}$ is identically equal to zero. The gradient, which is a conservative vector field since the curl of the gradient is identically equal to zero, meets both of these conditions. Problems with unwrapping occur at points where $\boldsymbol{F}$ contains a rotational vector component in addition to the phase gradient. This is where the fact that the phase is *defined* as a function of the complex field becomes important since branch points, which cause rotational components in the phase, are shown to occur at locations where the complex field goes to zero [31,33]. Fortunately, the two conditions above for path independence of the unwrapping line integral provide guidance in solving the unwrapping problem when $\boldsymbol{F}$ is not conservative. Equation (98) provides a way of identifying path dependence in an unwrapping problem, and Eq. (99) suggests methods for unwrapping the phase correctly even when the solution depends on the path.

Ghiglia and Pritt apply the theory of complex functions to derive an expression for the wrapped phase Ψ of a complex function in the vicinity of a point where the amplitude of the complex function goes to zero. The analysis expands a bounded complex function $s(x,y)$ about an arbitrary complex value z_0 with a Laurent-series-expansion function $f(z, z^*)$. In the vicinity of z_0, z is also a function of its location (x,y) in $s(x,y)$. Therefore the complex distance $(z - z_0)$ from a point $z = s(x,y)$ to a nearby point $z_0 = s(x_0, y_0)$ is related to the spatial distance given by $[(x - x_0)^2 + (y - y_0)^2]^{1/2}$. When the complex function is identically zero at the point (x_0, y_0), the behavior of the complex function at nearby points is governed by the magnitude r and phase θ of the complex distance $(z - z_0)$. The wrapped phase at the points in the vicinity of a zero in the complex function is then given by

$$\Psi = \tan^{-1}[(2\alpha - 1)\tan\theta], \tag{100}$$

where $0 \leq \alpha \leq 1$ gives the weight of the contributions of the complex distance $(z - z_0)$ and the conjugate of that distance $(z - z_0)^*$ [33]. When $\alpha = 1$ then $\Psi = \theta$ (for small θ), and only the complex distance $(z - z_0)$ affects the wrapped phase. When $\alpha = 0 \rightarrow \Psi = -\theta$ and only the conjugate of the complex distance affects the wrapped phase [33].

Figure 11 shows a plot of what Ghiglia and Pritt call a typical local phase function that results from setting $\alpha = 1$ and $\theta = \tan^{-1}(\Im\{z - z_0\}/\Re\{z - z_0\})$ in

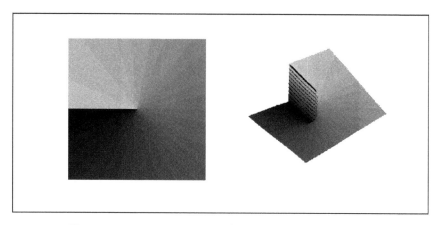

Figure 11:   Example of phase near a branch point

Eq. (100). The point where the complex function $s(x, y)$ goes to zero is located at the origin.[4] Integration of the gradient of the phase shown in Fig. 11 in a counterclockwise path that encloses the origin results in a value of 2π, which indicates that phase unwrapping depends on the path of integration. Ghiglia and Pritt call such points *phase residues* because they are analogous to the residues of complex functions. Contour integrals that contain a single phase residue are not equal to zero and, in fact, can only be equal to $\pm 2\pi$. The discontinuity that extends from the phase residue to the edge of the phase in Fig. 11 is called a *branch cut* because it indicates the transition between two branches, which are defined as the many different 2π intervals that contain equally valid solutions to functions of a complex variable z such as $\ln(z)$ or $\tan^{-1}(z)$ [13]. Points in a complex function that cannot be encircled without encountering a branch cut are called *branch points*, which is another term commonly used in AO literature for phase residues [13]. It is important to distinguish between branch cuts and *wrapping cuts* [86]. Both appear as lines (or cuts) defining 2π jumps in phase caused by restricting the phase values to a 2π interval. However, branch cuts indicate dependence of the unwrapping solution on the integration path and must not be crossed in performing the phase-unwrapping line integral in order to produce

---

[4]$\Re(u)$ was defined in Sec. 2.6 as returning the real part of a complex number u. Likewise, $\Im(u)$ returns the imaginary part of u.

consistent unwrapped phase solutions. Branch cuts terminate somewhere inside the wrapped phase while wrapping cuts either form closed paths or run from edge to edge in a truncated region of wrapped-phase measurements.

The directional derivative of the phase of an optical field with branch points violates Eq. (99), which suggests the existence of vector components in addition to the gradient. The directional derivative of such a field could be represented as the sum of the contributions of the gradient and curl components, i.e. [29]

$$\boldsymbol{F} = \nabla\phi + \nabla \times \boldsymbol{F}. \tag{101}$$

Equation (101) gives a more appropriate expression for the directional derivative of phase for a wavefront that has propagated through strong turbulence. In order to estimate the wavefront, a WFS must be able to measure both components in Eq. (101). Applying the phase-unwrapping line integral of Eq. (97) to phase with branch points by replacing $\nabla\phi$ with $\boldsymbol{F}$ leads to the unwrapping integral

$$\phi_{\mathrm{UW}} = \int_C \nabla\phi \cdot \mathrm{d}\boldsymbol{r} + \int_C \nabla \times \boldsymbol{F} \cdot \mathrm{d}\boldsymbol{r} + \phi(\boldsymbol{r}_0). \tag{102}$$

Therefore, the unwrapped phase ϕ_{UW} can be found by summing the *irrotational* part of the phase found by integrating the phase gradient, the *rotational* part of the phase associated with non-zero values of $\nabla \times \boldsymbol{F}$, and the offset $\phi(\boldsymbol{r}_0)$.

The unwrapping integral for the irrotational phase is independent of the path, but this is not true for the rotational phase. If the irrotational phase is isolated and unwrapped separately, the rotational phase is found by subtracting the irrotational phase from the original wrapped phase [86]. One common approach to unwrapping the irrotational phase defines a system of difference equations for the phase gradient and then solves this system using least-squares methods. Least-squares unwrapping produces phase estimates at each point as the average value of the line integral of Eq. (97) computed over every possible path leading to each point from the location of the offset $\phi(\boldsymbol{r}_0)$ [29]. If the phase has no rotational part, the least-squares solution is the exact unwrapping solution, since integration over every path in a conservative field results in exactly the same value. Therefore, the least-squares unwrapper provides a means of isolating the gradient of the phase and unwrapping it separately. The unwrapped phase can then be found from

$$
\begin{aligned}
\phi_{\mathrm{UW}} &= \phi_{\mathrm{LS}} + \phi_{\mathrm{R}} \\
&= \phi_{\mathrm{LS}} + \mathrm{W}\left[\phi_{\mathrm{W}} - \phi_{\mathrm{LS}}\right],
\end{aligned}
\tag{103}
$$

where ϕ_{LS} is the least-squares-phase-unwrapping solution, and ϕ_{R} is the rotational part of the phase found from subtracting the ϕ_{LS} from the original, wrapped phase ϕ_{W} and wrapping the result, which is indicated in Eq. (103) by the wrapping operator $\mathrm{W}[\cdot]$ [53,60]. This dissertation refers to this method as the least-squares principal value (LSPV) unwrapper.

The reason the local phase function in Fig. 11 is called typical becomes clear after observing rotational phases from simulated atmospheric propagation through strong turbulence. Figure 12 shows the rotational phase from a simulated field generated by numerical propagation of a point source through atmospheric phase screens with a total-path r_0 of 7.5cm over a distance of 15km. This clearly shows multiple branch points connected by branch cuts. As with the typical local phase function shown in Fig. 11, integration of the gradient of this phase in a counterclockwise path enclosing each branch point results in a value of $\pm 2\pi$.

2.8.2 Phase Reconstruction from Slope Measurements.   The SH WFS does not measure the phase directly, but instead measures the wavefront slope, which is related to the phase of the incident optical field. Phase reconstruction from Shack-Hartmann slope measurements is similar to the phase-unwrapping problem addressed in the previous section. However, unlike phase unwrapping, which integrates wrapped gradients computed from wrapped phase measurements, the Shack-Hartmann WFS

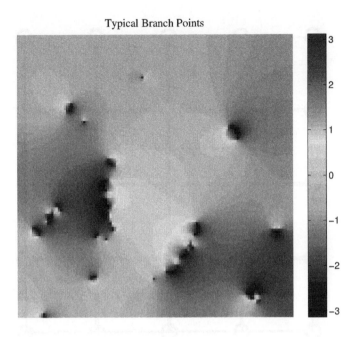

Figure 12:   Branch cuts in atmosperic phase

uses measurements that contain phase-gradient information. The SH phase-gradient measurements depend on their alignment with DM actuators, which is where the phase must be estimated. In the earliest days of AO research, Fried, Southwell, and Hudgin all recognized that least-squares reconstruction provided an effective means of estimating phase from slope measurements, and each proposed different alignment geometries [28, 40, 76].

Fried's geometry (Fig. 13) places the phase estimates (indicated by circles in Fig. 13) at the corners of the subapertures, the centers of which are the assumed locations of the SH sensor's horizontal and vertical slope measurements (indicated in Fig. 13 by right- and up-pointing arrows) [28]. In Fried's approach, the slopes are related to the average differences between phase values at the subaperture corners. For example, the phase values at the corners of the upper-left subaperture are related

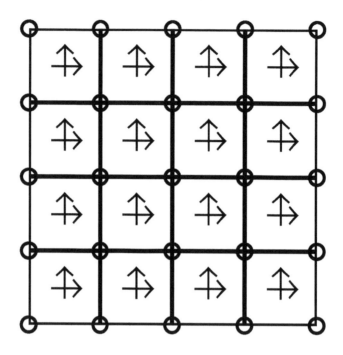

Figure 13:   Fried's alignment geometry.

to the slope measurements at the center of that subaperture by

$$s_1 = \frac{1}{2} \left(\phi_6 - \phi_1 + \phi_7 - \phi_2 \right)$$
$$s_{17} = \frac{1}{2} \left(\phi_1 - \phi_2 + \phi_6 - \phi_7 \right), \tag{104}$$

where the phase values ϕ_i are elements of a vector containing the 25 phase estimates ordered by column-major order (up $\rightarrow$ down, left $\rightarrow$ right), and s_1 and s_{17} are elements of a slope-measurement vector containing the horizontal slope measurements in elements 1–16 and vertical-slope measurements in elements 17–32, also in column-major order.

The alignment of slope measurements and phase estimates for the Hudgin geometry is illustrated in Fig. 14, where again circles indicate phase estimates and arrows indicate slope measurements. Using a similar ordering scheme to that described above

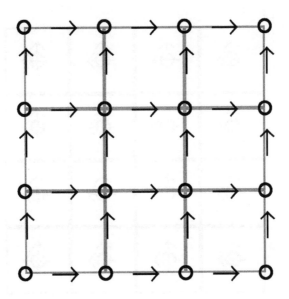

Figure 14: Hudgin's alignment geometry.

for Eq. (104), the slope measurements and phase estimates for the upper-left subaperture are related to each other in the Hudgin geometry by

$$
\begin{aligned}
s_1 &= \phi_5 - \phi_1 \\
s_2 &= \phi_6 - \phi_2 \\
s_{13} &= \phi_1 - \phi_2 \\
s_{16} &= \phi_5 - \phi_6.
\end{aligned}
\tag{105}
$$

In this case, there is a separate equation for each slope measurement since the differences between phase values at the subaperture corneres are not averaged together as is done in the Fried geometry [40]. Again, for Eq. (105) the phase-estimate and slope-measurement vectors are ordered using a column-major order; the horizontal slopes are in elements 1–12 of the slope vector, and the vertical slopes in elements 13–24.

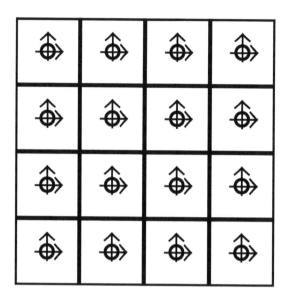

Figure 15:   Southwell's alignment geometry.

The Hudgin geometry can only be directly applied to slope measurements when the horizontal- and vertical-slope sensors can be aligned separately. Since the SH sensor's horizontal- and vertical-slope measurements are co-located, the Hudgin geometry cannot be used directly with SH measurements. However, the Southwell geometry introduces the intermediate step of averaging together slope measurements from adjacent SH subapertures, which then allows application of the Hudgin geometry to reconstruct phase estimates at the centers of the SH subapertures [76]. Figure 15 illustrates the location of slope measurements and phase estimates for the Southwell geometry. Overlaying the Hudgin and Southwell geometries, shown in Fig. 16 (Hudgin in gray, Southwell in black), illustrates how the two geometries ultimately use the same reconstruction approach, except that the Southwell geometry includes the intermediate step of averaging adjacent SH slope measurements.

Once an alignment geometry is selected, a linear system of equations can be written using either Eq. (104) or Eq. (105), as appropriate. This system of equations

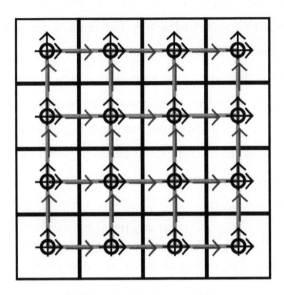

Figure 16: Overlaid Hudgin and Southwell geometries.

can then be used to solve for the phase using least-squares-error minimization, which can be implemented for fast computation with linear-algebra techniques [15,76]. Note that in the earlier discussion on phase unwrapping, least-squares techniques were used to estimate the unwrapped phase from the wrapped phase differences. In fact, phase unwrapping generally involves the computation and wrapping of adjacent phase differences followed by the application of the Hudgin-geometry reconstructor to the wrapped phase differences.

Fried and Hudgin both developed expressions numerically from simulation data for noise-propagation error associated with their reconstruction approaches [28,40,50]. Motivated by their work, Noll analytically derived a general expression for the noise-propagation error of least-squares reconstruction techniques [50]. Later, Wallner showed that when least-squares reconstruction is performed with an optimized, closed-loop control law, noise-propagation error depends only on the density of actuators and is no longer sensitive to the alignment geometry [88]. Hunt and Southwell achieved similar results for noise-propagation error using a matrix formulation of least-squares reconstruction, which also presented a very fast method for wavefront reconstruction [15, 76]. In all cases, the noise-propagation error increased in proportion to a very small, constant factor multiplied by the natural logarithm of the number of phase estimates across the WFS. Therefore, phase-reconstruction can actually attenuate noise for WFS's with relatively few subapertures and only begins to amplify noise for large numbers of subapertures. Even then, the noise-propagation factor is generally only slightly more than unity. For example, Hudgin's expression for noise-propagation error is given by [40]

$$\epsilon = 0.561 + 0.103 \ln N, \tag{106}$$

where N is the number of phase estimates across a dimension of the WFS (*i.e* N^2 is the total number of phase estimates). Therefore, when there are a large number of subapertures, a WFS in the Hudgin geometry, *e.g.* a WFS with 4096 phase estimates, results in a noise propagation factor about one, *e.g.* $\epsilon = 0.989$ for 4096-phase-estimate WFS. The noise-propagation error increases to only 1.06 for 16,384 phase estimates, which is an extremely large number of subapertures. Therefore, for practical WFS's, noise-propagation error of wavefront reconstructors does not generally amplify measurement error.

III. Review of Related Research

The literature review supplied motivation for a hybrid WFS, identified the best candidates for inclusion in a hybrid WFS, identified gaps in published work that needed to be filled in order to design a hybrid WFS, provided the analytical foundation for designing a hybrid WFS, and surveyed published attempts to combine the WFS's selected for inclusion in the hybrid WFS. Based on the information presented in Ch. II, the primary requirements of the hybrid WFS were identified as improved performance over previously-studied WFS's in strong scintillation and the potential for effective wavefront sensing with extended beacons. As indicated in the background material, the SH and SRI WFS's were identified as the best way to meet these requirements. Therefore, this review of related research is organized as follows: The first section presents a brief discussion of research related to effective wavefront sensing with extended beacons to justify inclusion of the SH WFS in the hybrid. The second section discusses the reported impact of scintillation on WFS's. The third section summarizes reported research on the SRI. The fourth section presents relevant research regarding the SH WFS. The last section discusses recent efforts that have actually combined the SRI and SH WFS's.

3.1 Extended Beacons

This work does not explore approaches to using the hybrid WFS with extended sources, but the SH WFS was selected for use in the hybrid WFS so that future work could continue in this area. Since extended-beacon capabilities were only motivation for inclusion of the SH WFS, a comprehensive review of literature on the subject is not presented here. However, for those interested in exploring the hybrid WFS's performance with extended beacons, a good starting point is provided by Poyneer, who summarized the most promising approaches to the estimation of wavefront slopes from Shack-Hartmann data using extended beacons. Her analysis showed how slope-estimation performance depends on scene content and scales with illumination [56]. The various methods she discusses for wavefront sensing with extended

75

beacons include maximum-likelihood estimation, deconvolution, and minimum-least-squares matching of subaperture images. Poyneer favored the least-squares-matching approach over the MLE approach due to issues related to computational cost, and she rejected deconvolution because of its poor noise-propagation characteristics [56]. The least-squares-matching approach maximizes the correlation between subaperture images and is implemented using fast Fourier transforms [56]. Later experimental results showed correlation-based WFS's produced more accurate, more robust, and less noisy slope measurements than a centroiding algorithm, even when using a point source [58]. Furthermore, correlation algorithms enable slope measurements from an extended source. Correlation-based slope sensing could be improved further to improve the hybrid WFS's performance. For example, Cain's approach uses an image-projection technique and maximum-likelihood estimation that incorporates previous measurements to greatly increase the speed and accuracy of correlation-based WFS's [17].

In summary, it has been well-established in the literature that SH WFS's can be effective with extended beacons. The references cited here are only examples to illustrate this and justify the choice of the SH WFS for inclusion in the proposed hybrid WFS.

3.2 Wavefront Sensors in Strong Scintillation

Fried and Vaughn showed that scintillation causes branch points and branch cuts in the phase of propagated wavefronts [31]. Their initial response to the problem of branch cuts was to position them so that they mainly ran along areas of low intensity, which minimized the unavoidable errors associated with placing the discontinuous branch cuts on a continuous-facesheet DM [31]. This, of course, assumed that the branch cuts could be sensed by the WFS. Later, Fried explored the issue of branch points further and found that they prevent complete reconstruction of the wavefront from slope measurements using least-squares reconstructors due to the existence of a 'hidden' phase that contains the branch points and branch cuts [29]. This phase is only hidden in the sense that least-squares methods cannot reconstruct it from slope measurements, since, when branch points are present, the curl term of Eq. (101) is not equal to zero (see Sec. 2.8). Fried also developed a closed-form solution for the hidden phase and used it to suggest a branch-point-tolerant wavefront reconstructor that required knowledge of branch-point locations [29]. In related work, Tyler formulated the problem of hidden phase in terms of slope discrepancy, which is the difference between slope measurements from a WFS and the gradient of the WFS's reconstructed phase [81]. Tyler used Fourier analysis to decompose WFS slope measurements into a gradient component, which he showed was identical to the least-squares-reconstructed phase, and the slope discrepancy, which includes the curl term of Eq. (101) as well as noise and fitting error. These observations were very similar to Fried's, but Tyler also developed a wavefront reconstructor that estimated both the gradient and curl components of the phase without needing to know the location of branch points. Soon after, Fried published a report that described the complex exponential reconstructor, which was a multigrid method of reconstructing the least-squares and hidden phase from slope measurements that was originally developed but never published by Itek Corporation during the 1980's [30]. Barchers and Fried *et al.* reported wave-optics results on the performance of the complex exponential reconstructor in the Fried and Hudgin geometries [4, 5]. These studies showed that the complex exponential reconstructor had some success in reconstructing the hidden phase especially when using slope measurements from a lateral-shearing interferometer (LSI). However, phase reconstructed from SH slope measurements remained sensitive to scintillation, especially at Rytov numbers greater than 0.2 and when d/r_0 was larger than 1/4 [3, 5]. The LSI performed better than the SH WFS with the complex exponential reconstructor but still showed sensitivity to scintillation and actually did worse than the least-squares reconstructor when $d/r_0 > 1/2$ [3, 4].

It is important to note that the studies discussed above examined the impact of scintillation on the formulation error of slope sensors. Formulation error is the error associated with the mathematical formulation of WFS measurements and represents the ideal case. Therefore, the problems suffered by slope sensors in strong scintillation are fundamental, and no amount of clever manipulation of intensity data to produce improved SH slope measurements (*e.g.* windowing, subaperture weighting, or Fourier analysis) is expected to alleviate them.

3.3   Self-Referencing Interferometer

Motivated by the poor performance of slope sensors in strong turbulence and strong scintillation, the Air Force Research Laboratory's (AFRL) Starfire Optical Range (SOR) began work on a WFS inspired by the PDI concept [63]. The formulation error of the PDI had been shown to be insensitive to scintillation and therefore showed promise for providing improved performance in extended-turbulence conditions [6, 63]. Wave-optics results confirmed this and showed that the SRI clearly outperformed slope sensors in strong scintillation even when the slope sensors used a complex-exponential reconstructor [3]. However, the comparison study also showed that the SH WFS using a least-squares reconstructor provided the best performance at large values of d/r_0 and weak scintillation [3]. This observation was one of the first motivations for consideration of a hybrid WFS.

Since the SRI concept proved promising theoretically, SOR developed a prototype and test facility to demonstrate it and evaluate its performance [63]. Published reports about the SRI during this period concentrated on comparison of temporal versus spatial phase-shifting approaches and the impact of optical amplification of the reference beam [18, 63, 64]. While temporal phase shifting was shown to have some benefits, spatial phase shifting appears to have been favored since it is less sensitive to temporal atmospheric effects and showed superior performance in laboratory demonstrations [6, 18, 64]. Laboratory demonstrations of the SRI also showed a sensitivity to scintillation that was not predicted by previous theoretical work [18]. This result clearly showed room for further analysis of SRI wavefront-estimation errors.

Several issues stand out as potential reasons for the discrepancy between the theoretical predictions of SRI performance and the laboratory observations. First of all, the theoretical studies, and even the wave-optics simulations, only addressed formulation error. This is the error associated with the mathematical formulation of SRI WFS measurements as the subaperture-averaged optical field. None of the published theoretical or simulation work actually implemented a four-bin, phase-shifting phase-estimation algorithm. Another issue is that the metric used to evaluate SRI performance in the analytical work was the field-estimation Strehl ratio, which provides a measure of how well the WFS estimates the real and imaginary parts of the incident optical field. The laboratory demonstration, by practical necessity, used Strehl ratio of the DM-corrected beam as the performance metric. To control a DM, the SRI field measurements must be converted into phase estimates, which was not directly addressed by the analytical work. Finally, the primary impact of scintillation addressed by the theoretical and simulation studies was that associated with branch points and branch cuts. The only study on the impact of noise on SRI measurements quantified it with the field-estimation Strehl ratio and did not include random fluctuations of classical intensity as a noise source [64]. Because these studies concentrated only on formulation error and field-estimation Strehl ratio, they did not adequately address the combined impact of scintillation and sensor noise on phase estimation. The fundamentally random process of photodetection combined with random fluctuations of classical intensity is well-documented [34]. Therefore, this was identified as an area of research that should be pursued to properly design a hybrid WFS. Also, because phase must be estimated in order to control a DM, the impact of SRI phase-estimation error was identified as requiring investigation before design of the hybrid WFS could begin. Both of these areas of research are addressed by the work presented in Ch. V of this dissertation.

3.4 Shack-Hartmann Wavefront Sensor

The SH WFS has been in wide use for a long time. Not surprisingly, an enormous body of work exists that analyzes it from numerous perspectives, and numerous ways of improving its performance have been proposed. Therefore, it is impractical to present an exhaustive review of literature related to the SH WFS. Also, since the focus of this work has been on modelling noise rather than improving the performance of a SH WFS, the centroid method of computing wavefront slopes from SH intensity images was selected as the mode of operation for the hybrid WFS's SH sensor. Because a detailed listing of work related to improving SH slope measurements or optimally reconstructing them into wavefront estimates would be extraneous, it is not included here. However, a great deal of such work was reviewed, and good examples are found in [8], [17], [26], [41], [57], [70], and [79], just to list a few.

While explorations into the limitations of Shack-Hartmann WFS's in scintillation have generally not included sensor noise (see Sec. 3.2), there is a significant body of published work on noise-induced centroid error in the absence of scintillation. Tyler and Fried address position-measurement error associated with white detector noise for a quad cell in [83]. In [91] Winick derives an expression for the CRLB for the shot-noise-induced variance of Gaussian-spot position measurements using an infinite detector array with non-negligible dark current. In Appendix A of [36], Hardy derives a general expression for image position measurement error, which turns out to be identical to Winick's CRLB when a Gaussian spot is used for the image function and dark current is neglected. In [66] Roddier presents a rule of thumb for slope error associated with noise-induced position error. Irwan and Lane emphasize the significance of spot shape and detector array size on centroid measurement error in [41] and develop expressions for optimizing performance with the appropriate selection of key parameters. Tyler discusses these types of errors in terms of their contributions to slope discrepency, which he points out are insignificant compared to the slope discrepancy associated with branch points [81]. In [79], Thomas *et. al.* conduct a comprehensive review of centroid computation and optimization algorithms that are all rooted in the latest understanding of noise-induced centroid errors. While this discussion by no means includes all work related to centroid-measurement errors, these references represent a core collection of useful insights for optimally designing Shack-Hartmann WFS's *given a deterministic intensity.*

In the past five years, WFS research has begun to explore the impact of scintillation and extended beacons. For example, Thomas *et al.* reported work on optimal wavefront sensing with elongated laser guide stars. [78]. Also, Robert *et al.* and Vedrenne *et al.* have reported work that provides analytical models for the impact of scintillation-induced slope errors on SH wavefront estimation when using extended sources as the beacon [65,85]. However, what appears to be lacking in the literature is a simple treatment of the interaction between photodetection noise and random intensity fluctuations and the impact of this coupling on the fidelity of SH slope measurements. In order to design a hybrid WFS that meets the stated requirements, a model for such error is necessary. Chapter IV presents the results of work that addressed this need.

3.5 *Work Combining WFS's for Deep Turbulence*

Combining multiple WFS's is not a new idea. Roggemann and Schulz combined Shack-Hartmann slope measurements with a conventional image to extend the dynamic range of the Shack-Hartmann WFS [67,68]. Patterson and Dainty presented a means of using a Shack-Hartmann WFS with astigmatic lenslets and subaperture quad-cell detectors to simultaneously measure both phase gradients and curvature and showed improved sensitivity of mirror modes for a membrane DM [51]. Phillips and Cain combined pupil- and image-plane data in a maximum-likelihood estimator to extract images from laser detection and ranging (LADAR) data in a post-processing algorithm that is less sensitive to atmospheric turbulence than deconvolution [54].

More recent work has been published reporting efforts to combine an SRI and a SH WFS in a hybrid approach for mitigating the performance degradation caused by extended-turbulence conditions. Belen'kii *et al.* report positive results in a laboratory demonstration of a conventional SRI-based AO system combined with an off-axis SH WFS used in a wavefront-based stochastic, parallel gradient descent (SPGD) algorithm [10]. The wavefront-based-SPGD (WBSPGD) approach is used in an AO system designed to pre-compensate a laser beam in order to achieve a high concentration of energy within the smallest area possible at a target. In WBSPGD, the WFS views the laser return from off-axis so that it does not 'see' the DM. Measurements from the WFS are then used to form a single metric that is optimized by controlling the DM actuators with the SPGD algorithm. Since the goal of WBSPGD is the highest possible concentration of energy at the target, the WFS metric is formed to provide information about the spot size at the target. Based on the principle that high-spatial-frequency phase fluctuations are averaged out over the finite extent of extended beacons, Belen'kii et al. selected the inverse of the aperture-averaged local-wavefront slope variance as the metric to minimize with SPGD [10,11]. In their experiment, they used a thermal-blooming cell to spread the outgoing laser and phase wheels etched to have Kolmogorov statististics to simulate atmospheric turbulence. In the hybrid system described by Belen'kii et al., the WBSPGD AO corrects beam spread due to beacon anisoplanatism and thermal blooming so that the conventional AO system can work with a beacon that is much closer to being a point source [12]. The reason for choosing the SRI as the WFS used in the conventional AO system was not discussed [10]. However, since the SRI is designed to operate with a point-source beacon, it seems likely that the WBSPGD approach was, in part, developed to assist an SRI-based AO system. Belen'kii et al. reported results for the WBSPGD acting alone and showed that it did indeed decrease spot size and increase intensity at the target compared to an uncompensated beam. They also showed results for the hybrid compared to an uncorrected beam and noted significant improvement (maximum performance gain of 4.9 and mean performance gain of 2.1) [10]. The hybrid system also did notably better than the WBSPGD alone. Unfortunately, they did not compare the hybrid results to the SRI-based AO system operating alone, so it must simply be inferred that the hybrid performed better than the stand-alone SRI would have since it was operating with a better beacon.

The work of Belen'kii et al. demonstrates the feasibility of a hybrid WFS that uses measurements from a SH WFS to condition the beacon so that an SRI-based AO system can operate effectively. This concept is related to the motivation for using a

SH WFS to eventually aid in extended-beacon wavefront sensing with the hybrid WFS proposed in this work. However, the hybrid approach proposed by Belen'kii *et al.* is dramatically different from the hybrid approach explored in this dissertation. First of all, the WBSPGD concept requires the SH WFS to be placed off-axis. The hybrid approach proposed in Ch. VI places both WFS pupils optically conjugate to the DM plane and has them work in tandem to perform conventional, phase-conjugating AO. In fact, the hybrid WFS proposed in this work could be used in combination with the WBSPGD approach. Since WBSPGD does not result in perfect beacon conditioning, a hybrid WFS used in the conventional AO system could still provide performance improvements over stand-alone-SRI-based AO combined with WBSPGD.

3.6   Motivation for a Hybrid WFS

The intended purpose of a hybrid WFS is to improve performance over a range of scintillation strengths and open a way for operating in strong scintillation with extended beacons. A significant body of AO research related to strong scintillation, extended beacons, and beacon anisoplanatism has developed over the past 20 years in response to the identified need to perform AO in deep-turbulence conditions. Deep turbulence is characterized by a Rytov number much greater than one, which causes significant degradation of the beacon due to scintillation and also has a very small isoplanatic angle associated with it. This type of turbulence can easily develop for propagation paths as short as 2 kilometers at high C_n^2 values such as those that occur at low altitudes during the day time [59, 82]. Deep-turbulence applications also often rely on beacons formed by reflected sunlight, laser illumination, or infrared 'hot-spot' emission, which by their nature are extended sources [82]. This problem poses significant challenges that are very different from those addressed by conventional AO. One problem associated with extended beacons is beacon anisoplanatism, which occurs when the source used as a beacon has finite extent that exceeds the isoplanatic patch size of the atmosphere. This results in a field at the WFS pupil that is essentially the sum of wavefronts from a multitude of point sources that have experienced partially correlated atmospheric conditions. Research in this area has shown that information about the atmospheric conditions of the propagation path is lost due to beacon anisoplanatism, so conventional AO fails to determine the DM commands required to correct the atmospheric distortions [82]. Multiconjugate adaptive optics (MCAO) show promise for increasing the isoplanatic angle and mitigating the effects of beacon anisoplanatism [82]. MCAO involves the use of multiple DM's placed optically conjugate to a number of planes along the propagation path to perform atmospheric corrections in sections. One suggested method of implementing MCAO is to use range gating to produce multiple beacons by capturing Rayleigh-backscattered laser light at multiple points along the propagation path [82]. One application of this technique, called bootstrap-beacon AO, uses range gating of Rayleigh backscatter to close the AO loop on a beacon that is relatively close and then gradually moves the range gate further away to compensate over longer distances [73]. Another method does not require a WFS at all but uses an image metric and gradient-descent algorithms to apply the DM corrections [82]. WFS-based MCAO would be significantly limited by the high level of scintillation in the beacon, but it might be useful for partially compensating for the part of the atmosphere near the transmitting aperture [82]. Gradient-descent MCAO (or tomography) would most likely be limited to controlling a small number of actuators due to the scaling of convergence times with the number of actuators controlled. It may turn out that some combination of WFS-based MCAO and gradient-descent tomography along with irradiance-redistribution adaptive optics and branch-point-tolerant phase reconstructors will provide a solution to the problem of deep turbulence. The one lesson that is clear from reported research on the deep-turbulence problem is that the WFS's used must be able to deal with extended beacons and scintillation. These issues, along with the characteristics of the SH and SRI WFS's discussed in Secs. 2.5 and 2.6, motivated the design of the hybrid WFS.

IV. A Model for Shot-Noise-Induced Centroid Error

4.1 Introduction

Adaptive optics systems correct optical distortions caused by propagation of light through a turbulent atmosphere. AO can greatly improve image quality in ground-based astronomical telescopes, significantly decrease bit-error rates in free-space optical communication, and enable beam-projection applications over long distances or through strong turbulence. In such systems, scattered laser light is often used to provide the beacon for measuring atmospheric distortions. Propagation distances that are long enough for the beacon to become scintillated cause difficulties for the wavefront sensors used to measure the atmospheric distortion. This is particularly true for the Shack-Hartmann WFS, which has been shown to perform poorly at measuring scintillated optical fields [5]. One issue that impacts Shack-Hartmann performance involves reconstruction of branch cuts in the phase of a scintillated optical field. This issue has been a significant focus of research in wavefront reconstruction techniques for improving the performance of WFS's that operate in strong turbulence [3–5,30,31]. However, these studies only evaluated the impact of scintillation on intensity-weighted gradients and did not address errors of the centroid measurements themselves. The question remains as to how significantly sensor noise impacts Shack-Hartmann measurements in scintillation. This is an important question because the answer helps to better define the performance limitations of Shack-Hartmann sensors and also provides insight into optimum design of Shack-Hartmann sensors that may be required to operate in some level of scintillation.

While explorations into the limitations of Shack-Hartmann WFS's in scintillation have generally not addressed centroid error, there is a significant body of published work on noise-induced centroid error in the absence of scintillation. Tyler and Fried address position-measurement error associated with additive, white detector noise for a quad cell in [83]. In [91] Winick derives an expression for the Cramer-Rao lower bound (CRLB) for the shot-noise-induced variance of Gaussian-spot position measurements using an infinite detector array with non-negligible dark current. In

Appendix A of [36], Hardy derives a general expression for image position measurement error, which turns out to be identical to Winick's CRLB when a Gaussian spot is used for the image function and dark current is neglected. In [66] Roddier presents a rule of thumb for slope error associated with noise-induced position error. Irwan and Lane emphasize the significance of spot shape and detector array size on centroid measurement error in [41] and develop expressions for optimizing performance with the appropriate selection of key parameters. In [79], Thomas *et. al.* conduct a comprehensive review of centroid computation and optimization algorithms that are all rooted in the latest understanding of noise-induced centroid errors. While this discussion by no means includes all work related to centroid-measurement errors, these references represent a core collection of useful insights for optimally designing Shack-Hartmann WFS's *given a deterministic intensity.*

The work presented here deals with a fundamental measurement-noise-related limitation for a Shack-Hartmann sensor operating on a scintillated field. Specifically, an expression is developed for the first time that models the centroid error resulting from photon noise in the presence of atmospherically induced fluctuating intensity, *i.e.* scintillation. Because the number of photons per subaperture is closely tied to the size of the subapertures, a model for centroid error due to photon noise and scintillation becomes an important parameter in sensor design studies. This chapter presents a model for photon-noise induced centroid error that accounts for scintillation and compares it to results from wave-optics simulations. The model matches the simulation results reasonably well for $d/r_0 = 1/4, 1/2$ and 1 and for Rytov numbers from 0 to 1.5 and shows that for high enough photocounts, Shack-Hartmann centroid measurements are largely insensitive to scintillation. However, at lower photon levels, scintillation and photon noise can contribute significantly to overall centroid error.

A Shack-Hartmann sensor uses a lenslet array placed at the exit pupil of a telescope to segment an incident wavefront and measure local wavefront slopes. If the lenslet array samples the incident wavefront finely enough, the images produced by the lenslets (or subapertures) are nearly diffraction-limited spots, and each wavefront

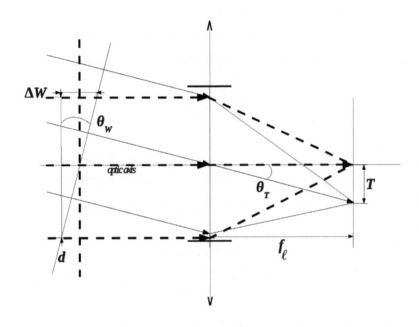

Figure 17:   Shack-Hartmann Subaperture Geometry

Wavefront slope θ_W is equal to the angular transverse spot displacement θ_T for a plane wave incident on a lenslet with focal length f_ℓ.

segment is well-approximated by a tilted plane wave. A photodetector array placed at the lenslets' common back focal plane provides a means of measuring the displacement of each subaperture spot. Figure 17 shows a geometric-optics ray diagram for a tilted plane wave incident on a single lenslet used to estimate wavefront slope from spot displacement. In this diagram, f_ℓ is the focal length [m] of the lenslet, ΔW is the optical pathlength difference (OPD) [m] between points on the wavefront separated by the distance d [m], θ_W is the angle between the wavefront and the pupil plane of the lenslet, and θ_T is the angle between the optical axis and a line from the center of the lenslet to the focused spot, which is displaced from the optical axis by the distance T [m]. The geometry shows that $\theta_W = \theta_T$ so that the wavefront slope is given by

$$\frac{\Delta W}{d} = \frac{T}{f_\ell}.$$

(107)

In the paraxial approximation, $\theta \approx \tan\theta$, so the wavefront slope can be approximated directly by θ_T. For a spot at the focal plane of a lenslet on which a tilted plane wave is incident, the angular measure of spot displacement in the x direction is given by the centroid

$$c_x = \frac{\int\limits_{-\infty}^{\infty}\!\!\int xI(x,y)\mathrm{d}x\mathrm{d}y}{\int\limits_{-\infty}^{\infty}\!\!\int I(x,y)\mathrm{d}x\mathrm{d}y},$$

(108)

where $I(x,y)$ is the intensity [W/sr], and x and y are angular coordinates [rad].

The photon-noise-limited variance of centroid measurements has been derived and presented in a number of references [36,91]. In these derivations, the shape of the image is assumed to be known and only its position is uncertain. While some sources address the impact of spot shape on centroid error, fluctuations of the spot shape are generally neglected [36,41,70,79]. Furthermore, the only source of variation in total photocount is assumed to be caused by detector noise. Under these assumptions, the variance due to Poisson-distributed photon noise can be written as [41]

$$\sigma_{c_x}^2 = \frac{1}{K} \iint\limits_{\mathcal{A}_{\text{det}}} x^2 f(x,y) \mathrm{d}x \mathrm{d}y, \tag{109}$$

where K is the total photocount within the subaperture, and $f(x,y)$ is a shape function for the intensity distribution. The shape function is normalized so that it integrates to unity. For a point-source beacon, $f(x,y)$ is the point-spread function (PSF) but can also be a general image function for estimating the position of an extended object. Equation (109) and similar expressions have been used to derive models that characterize the impact of a variety of parameters such as the size of detector-array pixels, the size of the detector array, the shape and size of the object or beacon, and the impact of optical aberrations. Because previous work on this type of centroid error is well-documented, it is not repeated here. Instead, the model proposed here applies only to WFS's that have already been designed to minimize the impact of these critical sources of centroid error.

The goal of the work presented here is to develop a model for centroid error that accounts for the doubly stochastic nature of centroid measurements when the incident optical field is scintillated. A model that includes scintillation should (and does) reduce to Eq. (109) in the absence of classical intensity fluctuations. Such a model enhances previously developed models by including the effect of scintillation. Also, because the doubly stochastic nature of centroid measurements for a scintillated field is due only to the photon noise and the classical intensity fluctuations, other sources of noise such as detector read noise and quantization error are not addressed here. Therefore, to isolate the centroid error due to photon noise from other sources of centroid error, the selected metric for the model developed in the following section is the centroid-error variance $\sigma_{\epsilon_x}^2$. This metric is the variance of the centroid error ϵ_x, which is defined as

$$\epsilon_x = c_{xN} - c_x, \tag{110}$$

where c_x is the centroid computed from intensity without shot noise, and c_{xN} is the centroid computed from Poisson-distributed photocounts of intensity.

4.2 Centroid-Error Variance in Scintillation

When stochastic fluctuations of classical intensity are present, photocount statistics must be considered to be based on a conditional probability distribution [34]. The unconditional statistics of photocounts K are determined by marginalizing the conditional probability of K over the statistics of *integrated intensity*, which is the intensity integrated over the detector solid angle $\mathcal{A}_{\mathrm{det}}$ and integration time τ. Therefore, the analysis must account for the conversion of integrated intensity into photocounts, which is facilitated by definition of the factor

$$\alpha = \frac{\eta_q}{hc/\lambda}, \tag{111}$$

where $\eta_q \leq 1$ is the detector quantum efficiency, h is Planck's constant [6.626196×10^{-34} J·sec], c is the speed of light in vacuum [$\approx 2.998 \times 10^8$ m/sec], and λ is the optical wavelength [m].

The angular measure for the x-component of the centroid of a spatial-intensity-distribution function $I(x, y)$ is given by Eq. (108). If the spatial distribution of intensity is adequately sampled, the centroid can be estimated using a discrete $N \times N$ photodetector array by replacing the integrals over the intensity in the centroid equation with photocount summations, i.e.

$$\hat{c}_x = \frac{\sum_{i=1}^{N^2} x_i K_i}{K}, \tag{112}$$

where x_i is the angular x-coordinate of the center of the ith pixel. For a given $I(x, y)$, the mean photocount of the ith pixel is given by

$$\langle K_i \rangle = \alpha \tau \int_{x_i - w_p/2}^{x_i + w_p/2} \int_{y_i - w_p/2}^{y_i + w_p/2} I(x, y) \mathrm{d}x\mathrm{d}y \tag{113}$$

90

where w_p is the angular extent of each dimension of a square pixel. This form assumes that intensity fluctuations have a minimal impact over the integration time. The assumption that intensity fluctuations are minimal over the duration of the integration time is valid either for point-source beacons with very long coherence times or for pseudothermal beacons with short coherence times relative to the integration time [34]. In the second case, WFS's require that the beacon's coherence time is shorter than the sensor's integration time, which must, in turn, be shorter than the temporal evolution of atmospheric phase disturbances, since these are what the WFS is measuring [87].

Equation (113) expresses the mean photocount of the ith pixel as the integral over a continuous intensity that is a function of position. However, to evaluate the behavior of the pixel photocounts over the statistics of spatially varying intensity, it is helpful to define mean pixel photocounts in terms of the total subaperture intensity I and shape function $f(x, y)$ as

$$
\begin{aligned}
\langle K_i \rangle &= \alpha \tau \mathcal{A}_{\text{det}} I \iint_{\mathcal{A}_i} f(x, y) \mathrm{d}x \mathrm{d}y \\
&= \alpha \tau \mathcal{A}_{\text{det}} I f_i,
\end{aligned}
\tag{114}
$$

where $\mathcal{A}_i$ is the solid angle of the ith pixel of the detector array and $f_i = \iint_{\mathcal{A}_i} f(x, y) \mathrm{d}x \mathrm{d}y$ is the fraction of light incident on the ith pixel. This definition of mean pixel photocounts can only be applied to subapertures that are small enough to ensure scintillation is well-correlated within a subaperture. Based on a model for aperture-averaging of scintillation presented in [1], scintillation can safely be assumed to be well-correlated over subapertures sized so that $d \leq r_0$.

To examine the centroid statistics, it is helpful to define a random variable c_i, which is the contribution from the ith pixel to the centroid calculation. For a given average subaperture photocount $\langle K \rangle = \sum_{i=1}^{N^2} \langle K_i \rangle$, the centroid represents a monotonic variable transformation of the pixel photocount K_i. Therefore, the expected value of c_i is given by

$$\langle c_i \rangle = \frac{x_i}{\langle K \rangle} \langle K_i \rangle, \tag{115}$$

and the variance is given by

$$
\begin{aligned}
\sigma_{c_i}^2 &= \left(\frac{x_i}{\langle K \rangle}\right)^2 \sigma_{K_i}^2 \\
&= \left(\frac{x_i}{\langle K \rangle}\right)^2 \langle K_i \rangle.
\end{aligned}
\tag{116}
$$

The assumed Poisson distribution of the photocounts has been used to set $\sigma_{K_i}^2 = \langle K_i \rangle$ in Eq. (116). Although the photocounts at individual pixels are closely related to one another through the shape function, the photocount *fluctuations* due to Poisson-distributed photon noise at different pixels are independent. Essentially, instead of assuming independent, identically distributed noise, this model assumes independent, deterministically distributed noise. When the detector array has a sufficient number of pixels, and the spot has a large number of photons, the centroid variance can be expressed as

$$\sigma_{c_x | b}^2 = \sum_{i=1}^{N^2} \left(\frac{x_i}{\langle K \rangle}\right)^2 \langle K_i \rangle. \tag{117}$$

Up to this point, the only source of randomness addressed has been photon noise, *i.e.* intensity and spot shape have been assumed to be deterministic. Use of the centroid-error metric defined in Eq. (110) removes any variation inherent in the centroid calculation and results in a metric for centroid-error variance that isolates the impact of photon noise. However, because photon noise is Poisson-distributed, it has a mean value that depends on the intensity of the incident light, which can also fluctuate randomly before photodetection. Therefore, Eq. (117) only gives a *conditional* variance [34]. This is why the subscript is written as $c_x | b$, where b is a vector representing all of the random parameters on which the variance given by Eq. (117) is conditioned. The unconditional variance of a random variable X given a particular value y for the random variable Y comes from the conditional variance formula

$$\sigma_X^2 = \mathrm{E}\left[(\mathrm{Var}(X|Y=y)] + \mathrm{Var}\left[\mathrm{E}(X|Y=y)\right],\right. \tag{118}$$

where $\mathrm{E}(\cdot)$ is the expected-value operation and $\mathrm{Var}(\cdot)$ is the variance operation [69]. The second term in Eq. (118) accounts for variation caused by a mean that has been conditioned on a random parameter. Therefore, the centroid error associated with intensity fluctuations and photon noise comes from averaging $\sigma_{c_x|b}^2$ over the randomly fluctuating intensity caused by scintillation. A fully unconditional model for centroid-error variance could theoretically be derived by successive application of the conditional-variance formula to multiple random parameters. However, such extensions of the model could be very difficult to achieve in practice. For example, for subaperture sizes larger than the atmospheric coherence cell (*i.e.* $d/r_0 > 1$), intensity fluctuations can also be caused by random variation in the spot shape. Inclusion of fluctuating intensity caused by random spot shape in the model for centroid-error variance would require an expression for the variance of the mean photocounts for all possible spot shapes, which would be a very difficult problem in itself. To simplify the model and obtain results that at least include the impact of scintillation, this work employs the widely used assumption that the spot shape does not fluctuate. Although the spots are broadened due to turbulence, they are assumed to have fixed shapes. Spot shape is analyzed in greater detail in Sec. 4.2.2 below.

Restricting attention to small subapertures ($d/r_0 \leq 1$) allows substitution of Eq. (114) for $\langle K_i \rangle$ in Eq. (117), so the conditional centroid variance can be written as

$$\sigma_{c_x|b}^2 = \frac{1}{\alpha \tau \mathcal{A}_{\mathrm{det}} I} \sum_{i=1}^{N^2} x_i^2 f_i. \tag{119}$$

Equation (119) allows $\sum x_i^2 f_i$ to be separated from the intensity I and placed outside integrals over the probability density function (pdf) of random intensity. Averaging Eq. (119) over the intensity results in the the unconditional centroid-error variance given by

$$\sigma_{\epsilon_x}^2 = \frac{\sum_i x_i^2 f_i}{\alpha \tau \mathcal{A}_{\text{det}}} \int_0^\infty \frac{1}{I} p_I(I) dI, \tag{120}$$

where $p_I(I)$ is the pdf of the randomly fluctuating classical intensity. Under the first-order Rytov approximation for light with phase and amplitude fluctuations caused by atmospheric turbulence, the classical intensity fluctuations follow a log-normal distribution [1]. Although experimental observations have shown that the log-normal pdf does not perfectly describe intensity fluctuations in strong scintillation, it results in tractable integrals that provide simple, closed-form expressions for the variance of intensity-based measurements such as the centroid. The log-normal pdf of intensity is given by

$$p_I(I) = \frac{1}{I\sigma\sqrt{2\pi}} \exp\left[\frac{-(\ln I - \mu)^2}{2\sigma^2}\right], \tag{121}$$

where μ and σ are parameters related to the intensity mean $\langle I \rangle$ and variance σ_I^2 by

$$
\begin{aligned}
\mu &= \ln\left(\frac{\langle I \rangle^2}{\sqrt{\sigma_I^2 + \langle I \rangle^2}}\right) \\
&= \ln\left(\frac{\langle I \rangle}{\sqrt{\tilde{\sigma}_I^2 + 1}}\right)
\end{aligned} \tag{122}
$$

and

$$
\begin{aligned}
\sigma^2 &= \ln\left(\frac{\sigma_I^2}{\langle I \rangle^2} + 1\right) \\
&= \ln\left(\tilde{\sigma}_I^2 + 1\right).
\end{aligned} \tag{123}
$$

In Eqs. (122) and (123), the log-normal-pdf parameters μ and σ have been expressed in terms of the scintillation index defined by [1]

$$\tilde{\sigma}_I^2 \triangleq \frac{\sigma_I^2}{\langle I \rangle^2}. \tag{124}$$

Substituting the log-normal pdf into Eq. (120) and performing the integration leads to the final expression for the unconditional centroid-error variance

$$
\begin{aligned}
\sigma_{\epsilon_x}^2 &= \frac{1}{\alpha \tau \mathcal{A}_{\text{det}}} e^{-\mu + \sigma^2/2} \sum_i x_i^2 f_i \\
&= \frac{1}{\langle K \rangle} \left(\tilde{\sigma}_I^2 + 1 \right) \sum_i x_i^2 f_i.
\end{aligned}
\tag{125}
$$

Equation (125) is the key result of this chapter. It expresses the centroid-error variance as a function of the average total number of photons incident on a subaperture, the distribution of the spot within the subaperture, and the scintillation index. For a continuous, infinite detector, Eq. (125) becomes

$$
\sigma_{\epsilon_x}^2 = \frac{1}{\langle K \rangle} \left(\tilde{\sigma}_I^2 + 1 \right) \iint\limits_{-\infty}^{\infty} x^2 f(x, y) \mathrm{d}x \mathrm{d}y,
\tag{126}
$$

which, in the absence of scintillation, reduces to Eq. (109). Therefore, previous expressions for centroid error that have neglected scintillation can include scintillation effects, assuming the intensity obeys a nearly log-normal distribution, by multiplying the no-scintillation centroid error by $(\tilde{\sigma}_I^2 + 1)$.

To illustrate the effectiveness of the centroid-error model in the absence of scintillation, Fig. 18 shows the model for centroid error (*a.k.a.* normalized position error) given by taking the square root of Eq. (125) (with $\tilde{\sigma}_I^2 = 0$) plotted as a function of pixel size, which is characterized in the plot by the number of pixels n_T per full width at half max (FWHM) of the assumed spot function. For these results, a Gaussian spot shape was used, both in the model and for the simulated spots. The plot shows simulation results (solid, gray line labeled 'Simulation Outcome' in the legend) and the Gaussian-spot approximation (dash-dotted, black line) computed from the closed-form expression of centroid error that results from assuming a Gaussian spot shape and continuous detector array and evaluating the resulting integral in Eq. (126). The simulations were performed by generating 500 realizations of a Gaussian spot sized

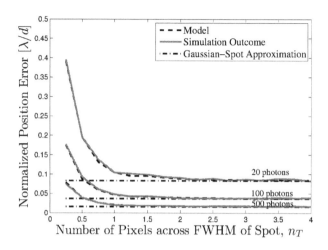

Figure 18:   Centroid Error Vs. Pixel Size

to match the central lobe of a diffraction-limited spot for a rectangular aperture with 20, 100, and 500 total photons incident on the subaperture. The spots were randomly positioned to be centered on average but have rms jitter in the x-direction equal to 0.1 times the pixel size and no jitter in the y-direction. Photon noise was simulated by passing the spots to a Poisson random-number generator. Similar results have been reported previously in [32] and [79], however these publications only showed simulation results and the value computed from the closed-form expression associated with a Gaussian-spot approximation. The dashed, black lines in Fig. 18 show the results of the suggested model, which were generated by actually performing the summation in Eq. (125) over an appropriately sized, normalized Gaussian spot. This shows that the model presented here matches simulation results better than previously-reported models, even for large pixels, where the closed-form expression fails to accurately predict the photon-noise-induced centroid error.

4.2.1 Impact of the Intensity Probability Density.   As mentioned above, some experiments have shown that the lognormal pdf does not always provide the most accurate description of intensity probability densities. A natural question arises as to how much of an impact the assumed intensity pdf has on the centroid-error variance model presented in the previous section. The gamma-gamma pdf has been suggested as an improvement over the lognormal pdf for the strong-scintillation regime [1]. Therefore, the gamma-gamma pdf is used here to derive a model for centroid-error variance. The result is significantly different from that reached using the lognormal pdf. The gamma-gamma pdf of intensity is expressed as

$$p_I(I) = \frac{2(\tilde{\alpha}\beta)^{(\tilde{\alpha}+\beta)/2}}{\Gamma(\tilde{\alpha})\Gamma(\beta)\langle I \rangle} \left(\frac{I}{\langle I \rangle}\right)^{(\tilde{\alpha}+\beta)/2-1} K_{\tilde{\alpha}-\beta}\left(2\sqrt{\tilde{\alpha}\beta I/\langle I \rangle}\right), I > 0, \tag{127}$$

where $\langle I \rangle$ is the expected value of intensity, $\tilde{\alpha}$ and β are parameters related to large- and small-scale atmospheric effects[1], $K_p(x)$ is a modified Bessel function of the second kind, and $\Gamma(z)$ is the gamma function [1]. For zero inner scale and a spherical-wave model, $\tilde{\alpha}$ and β are given by

$$\tilde{\alpha} = \left[\exp\left(\frac{0.20\ln(\tilde{\sigma}_I^2 + 1)}{\left\{1 + 0.19\left[\ln(\tilde{\sigma}_I^2 + 1)\right]^{6/5}\right\}^{7/6}}\right) - 1\right]^{-1}$$

$$\beta = \left[\exp\left(\frac{0.20\ln(\tilde{\sigma}_I^2 + 1)}{\left\{1 + 0.23\left[\ln(\tilde{\sigma}_I^2 + 1)\right]^{6/5}\right\}^{5/6}}\right) - 1\right]^{-1}. \tag{128}$$

Substituting the gamma-gamma pdf given by Eq. (127) into Eq. (120) and evaluating the integral leads to a model for the centroid-error variance. The integral over the gamma-gamma pdf can be solved using a table of integrals, {see Integral 16 of Appendix II in [1]}, which results in a centroid-error variance given by

$$\sigma_{\epsilon_x}^2 = \frac{\sum_i x_i^2 f_i}{\langle K \rangle} \left[\frac{\tilde{\alpha}\beta}{(\tilde{\alpha}-1)(\beta-1)}\right]. \tag{129}$$

This model for centroid-error variance behaves very differently in strong turbulence from the model given by Eq. (125).

---

[1]The notation $\tilde{\alpha}$ is used to distinguish large-scale atmospheric effects from the quantum conversion factor defined in Eq. (111).

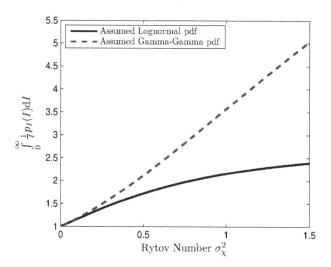

Figure 19:   Impact of Intensity pdf on Centroid-Error Model

Figure 19 plots Eqs. (125) and (129) (normalized by $\sum_i x_i^2 f_i / \langle K \rangle$) over a range of values for the Rytov number σ_χ^2. These results indicate that the form of the pdf used can have a drastic impact on the model of centroid-error variance. Although the expressions above for $\tilde{\alpha}$ and β were developed from theory, Andrews and Phillips report in [1] that these parameters actually had to be adjusted to achieve a match between theory and experimental results. The important point here is that the assumed pdf of intensity has a significant impact on the model for centroid-error variance. However, both the lognormal and gamma-gamma pdf's result in a model for centroid-error variance that captures its dependence on scintillation strength. The intensity pdf's computed for wave-optics data presented in Sec. 4.3 match the lognormal pdf more closely than the gamma-gamma pdf, so Eq. (125) was used as the model for centroid-error variance. However, the lognormal pdf does not match the wave-optics data as well for small values of d/r_0, which also corresponds to an observed discrepancy between the model for centroid-error variance and that measured from the simulations. This is not caused by improper simulation methods but is an unavoidable artifact associated with random intensity fluctuations. Other authors have studied this issue with varying degrees of success at getting simulated pdf's to match theory [1, 23, 39].

A significant advantage of the approach to developing the model for centroid-error variance presented here is the ability to evaluate the impact of different intensity pdf's on centroid error. While it may be possible to develop models similar to the one given by Eq. (125) using heuristic arguments, such models could not necessarily be adjusted to account for different intensity pdf's.

4.2.2 Accounting for Atmospheric Spread in SH Spots. All previous studies on centroid error develop expressions that ultimately depend on the shape of the intensity function. Many investigators assume a Gaussian spot [91]. Others derive expressions in terms of the system optical transfer function (OTF), which is related to the PSF through a Fourier transform [83, 89]. Irwan and Lane use a similar approach to develop expressions for centroid error due to truncation by a finite detector array and photon noise that also account for atmospheric spread of the diffraction-limited spot for a circular aperture [41]. Thomas *et al.* develop an expression for the diffraction-limited spot of a square aperture that estimates the impact of photon noise on centroid error, which scales with detector-array size [79]. However, Eq. (125) is general, so any shape function can be used for $f(x, y)$ in the integral over pixel area to determine the values for f_i. With the speed and precision of modern computers, numerical integration over a given shape function provides a suitable means of evaluating Eq. (125). The centroid-error-variance model compared against wave-optics results in Sec. 4.3 is computed in just this way using a $sinc^2$ function. Since phase effects have a much greater impact on spot shape, and thereby centroid error, than intensity effects (such as scintillation) [35], the model needs to account for non-diffraction limited spot shapes caused by phase aberrations. However, at subaperture sizes $d \leq r_0$, the phase effects are relatively small and primarily result in a spreading of the spot without significantly changing its shape or causing it to break up. The model for centroid-error variance due to scintillation and photon noise is adjusted to account for subaperture aberrations caused by the atmosphere by adjusting a width parameter in the shape function.

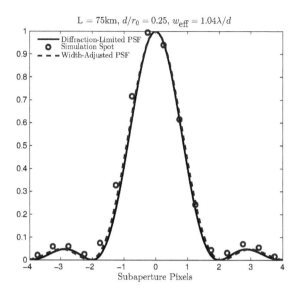

Figure 20:   Shack-Hartmann Subaperture Average Spot Shape, $d/r_0 = 1/4$

Figures 20 through 22 illustrate the spreading of spots in SH subapertures as d/r_0 increases. In Shack-Hartmann WFS's with square subapertures, the spot-shape function is

$$f(x, y, w) = \text{sinc}^2 \left(\frac{x}{w} \right) \text{sinc}^2 \left(\frac{y}{w} \right), \tag{130}$$

where w is the width of the spot. In a diffraction-limited, square subaperture with side length d and focal length f_ℓ, $w = \lambda f_\ell / d$ (for spatial coordinate x specified in meters). If the subapertures were circular, the PSF's could be estimated by performing a Fourier-Bessel transform of the turbulent OTF [34]. However, because SH subapertures are square, Eq. (130) provides a more accurate estimate for the PSF. For square subapertures with $d \leq r_0$, aberrations due to atmospheric turbulence and scintillation can be accounted for by changing w to a value that generates a PSF that more closely approximates the system PSF. This effective spot width can be computed by

$$w_{\text{eff}} = w_{\text{DL}} \times \frac{\int\limits_{-\infty}^{\infty} \mathcal{H}_{\text{opt}}(f_X) \mathrm{d}f_X}{\int\limits_{-\infty}^{\infty} \mathcal{H}_{\text{opt}}(f_X) \mathcal{H}_{\text{atm}}(f_X) \mathrm{d}f_X}, \tag{131}$$

100

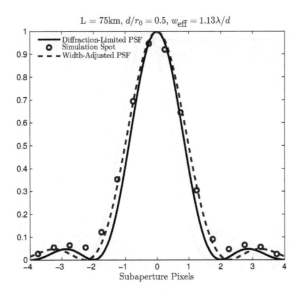

Figure 21: Shack-Hartmann Subaperture Average Spot Shape, $d/r_0 = 1/2$

where w_{DL} is the width parameter used for a diffraction-limited spot, $\mathcal{H}_{\mathrm{opt}}$ is the optical transfer function (OTF) of the optics, $\mathcal{H}_{\mathrm{atm}}$ is the OTF of the atmosphere, and $f_X = x/(\lambda f_\ell)$ is the spatial frequency component in the x-direction. Here x is in units of meters. For a square aperture, the one-dimensional OTF of the optics is given by

$$\mathcal{H}_{\mathrm{opt}}(f_X) = \Lambda\left(\frac{f_X}{2f_0}\right), \tag{132}$$

where $2f_0 = d/(\lambda f_\ell)$ is the spatial cutoff frequency, and $\Lambda(x)$ is the triangle function defined as [35]

$$\Lambda(x) = \begin{cases} 1 - |x| & |x| \leq 1 \\ 0 & \text{otherwise.} \end{cases} \tag{133}$$

The short-exposure OTF of the atmosphere is defined as

$$\mathcal{H}_{\mathrm{atm}}(\rho) = \exp\left\{-3.44\left(\frac{\rho}{r_0}\right)^{5/3}\left[1 - a\left(\frac{\rho}{d}\right)^{1/3}\right]\right\}, \tag{134}$$

101

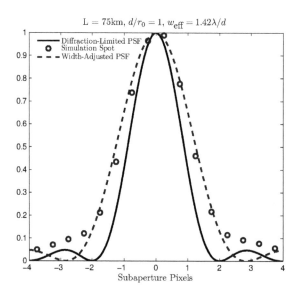

Figure 22:   Shack-Hartmann Subaperture Average Spot Shape, $d/r_0 = 1$

where $\rho = (f_X^2 + f_Y^2)^{1/2}$ is a radial spatial frequency coordinate, and a is a scintillation parameter; $a = 1$ in the absence of scintillation, and $a = 1/2$ when scintillation is present [34]. Equation (134) was derived by assuming a circular aperture [27].

Given a set of values for d, r_0, and a, the effective spot width w_{eff} can be computed by substituting Eqs. (132) and (134) into Eq. (131) and evaluating the integrals numerically. Figures 20 through 22 show plots of width-adjusted PSF's fit to the average spot shapes computed from wave-optics simulations for a point-source propagation over a 75km path length through atmospheric turbulence with $r_0 = 7.5$cm. The SH subapertures were sized to achieve $d/r_0 = 1/4$ (Fig. 20), $d/r_0 = 1/2$ (Fig. 21), and $d/r_0 = 1$ (Fig. 22). As d/r_0 increases, the spreading of the spot is clearly evident, but for $d/r_0 \leq 1$ the spots resemble a diffraction-limited shape closely enough to permit the approximation presented above, which leads to a close fit of the width-adjusted PSF to the central lobe of the average spots, as shown in Figs. 20 through 22. This approximation provides the benefit of a centroid model that can be quickly computed for a wide range of operating conditions and design parameters. When $d/r_0 > 1$, the plot in Fig. 22 suggests that the average spot may be better approximated by a function other than the sinc^2 function. Specifically, techniques involving inverse-Fourier transforms are discussed in [34] for approximating average PSF's that are the combination of a diffraction-limited "core" and a much broader "halo", which Fig. 22 suggests may be a better approximation for subaperture spots when $d/r_0 > 1$.

4.3   Testing the Model against Wave-Optics Simulations

4.3.1   Wave-Optics Atmospheric Propagations.   Wave-optics simulations provide a test of how well the model represents physical reality [25]. Atmospherically distorted optical fields were obtained by numerically propagating an on-axis point source through 40 atmospheric realizations, each modeled by ten Kolmogorov phase screens. The phase screens were evenly spaced throughout the propagation path and designed to provide a total-path atmospheric coherence width of $r_0 = 7.5$cm. The point source was propagated using the angular-spectrum form of the Huygens-Fresnel integral with multiple partial-propagation planes separated by distances and sampled with spacings designed to mitigate aliasing effects [19, 72]. For scintillation effects, the point source was propagated over eight different distances ranging from 5km to 75km in 10km increments. A 1024×1024 grid was used to propagate the point source to obtain optical fields at the observation plane inside a 256×256 central region of interest. The case of no scintillation was simulated using a complex field with uniform amplitude and phase from a single Kolmogorov phase screen.

The 256×256 optical fields, cropped from the propagated 1024×1024 fields, corresponded to a 1.2m square region so that partitioning these fields with a 16×16 array of subapertures resulted in $d/r_0 = 1$. Extracting smaller regions from the 256×256 fields enabled smaller values of d/r_0, but also resulted in fewer samples in the fields (128×128 samples for $d/r_0 = 1/2$ and 64×64 samples for $d/r_0 = 1/4$). Also, to maintain the same diffraction-limited spot size relative to the size of the pixels in the subaperture detector array, the focal length of the lenslets was adjusted for each different subaperture size (see Sec. 4.3.2). Therefore, to avoid aliasing in the propaga-

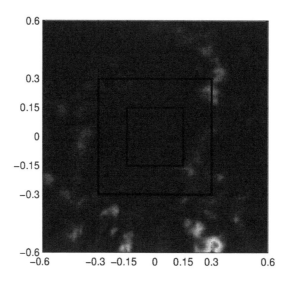

Figure 23:   Aperture Size in Wave-Optics Simulations

tion through the SH subapertures, the 256×256-sample fields were interpolated to a denser grid before extracting the central regions used to obtain smaller values of d/r_0. Figure 23 shows the sizes of the apertures used in the wave-optics simulations on an image of the field amplitude for a case of strong scintillation (75km propagation distance, Rytov number ≈ 1.5). As Fig. 23 shows, the extracted fields corresponded to 60cm and 30cm square regions for the $d/r_0 = 1/2$ and $d/r_0 = 1/4$ cases, respectively.

The fidelity of the atmospheric phase effects in the observation fields was evaluated by comparing the computed coherence factor of the fields with theoretical predictions. Also, since this work evaluates the behavior of the SH WFS in scintillation, the intensity pdf was plotted along with plots of the lognormal and gamma-gamma pdf's. Figure 24 shows these plots for the 75km propagation distance and $d/r_0 = 1$. This shows that the coherence factor matches theory exceptionally well in this case, and the intensity pdf is closely approximated by the lognormal pdf. While the gamma-gamma pdf is typically considered to be more appropriate for strong turbulence than the lognormal pdf, several authors have shown that getting wave-optics simulations to match any particular theoretical intensity pdf is challenging [1, 23, 39]. In fact, as

104

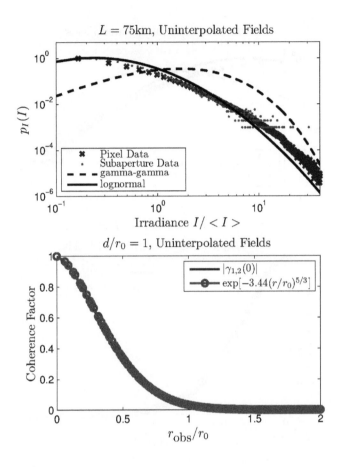

Figure 24: Uninterpolated Data Intensity and Phase Statistics, $d/r_0 = 1$

mentioned in Sec. 4.2.1, Andrews and Phillips had to adjust the $\tilde{\alpha}$ and β parameters in the gamma-gamma pdf empirically to obtain good agreement with simulations, rather than use the theoretically-calculated values [1]. Initial inspection of both the uninterpolated and interpolated fields extracted from the propagated fields to achieve smaller values for d/r_0 appeared to show similar fidelity. However, slight discrepancies between the centroid-error model and the wave-optics results, which are shown in Sec. 4.3.4, motivated closer inspection. Figures 25 and 26 show that the fidelity of the phase remains very good for both the uninterpolated and interpolated fields of the $d/r_0 = 1/4$ case. Figure 26 illustrates the impact of interpolation on the intensity

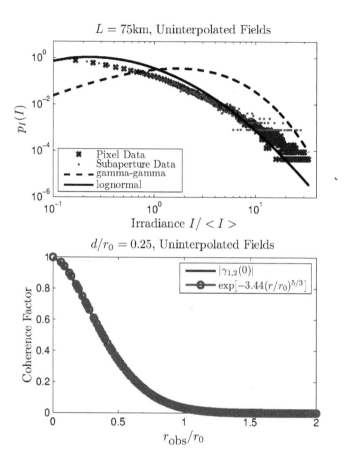

Figure 25: Uninterpolated Data Intensity and Phase Statistics, $d/r_0 = 1/4$

pdf (blue $\times$'s), but the subaperture-averaged intensity pdf (red dots) for the interpolated data (Fig. 26) is very similar to that for the uninterpolated data (Fig. 25). The most significant observations about the intensity pdf's in Figs. 24 through 26 are the deviation from the lognormal pdf caused by subaperture averaging and the deviation from the lognormal pdf with decreasing subaperture size.

As shown in Sec. 4.2.1, the intensity pdf can have a significant impact on the centroid-error variance. This deviation of the simulations' intensity pdf's from the assumed lognormal pdf seems to be the most likely explanation for the small amount of deviation between the centroid-error-variance model and the simulation results pre-

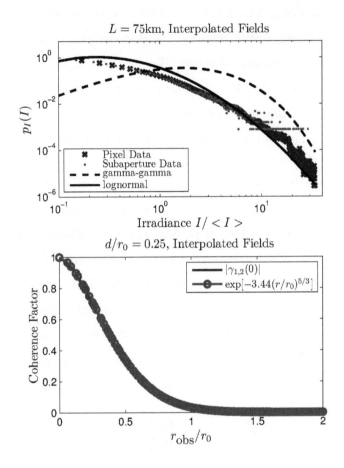

Figure 26: Interpolated Data Intensity and Phase Statistics, $d/r_0 = 1/4$

sented in Sec. 4.3.4. However, the discrepancy between the centroid-error model and the simulation results was small enough that further simulations aimed at achieving better fidelity of the intensity statistics were not warranted, especially since the behavior of intensity in strong scintillation is not well understood, and analytical models are based on heuristic arguments and experimental observations [1]. In fact, a number of authors have attempted to formulate expressions for statistical moments of intensity and/or intensity pdf's that match simulation and experiment [1, 23–25, 46]. Generally, simulation has matched experiment better than theory, and agreement has yet to be reached on a suitable form for intensity pdf's in the focusing and asymptotic regimes [1, 24]. In short, determining a suitable pdf of intensity in the presence of scintillation is an active area of research, and discrepancies between simulation and theory appear to be commonly observed. The method employed here to develop a model for photon-noise-induced centroid-error variance that accounts for scintillation permits adaptation of the model by substitution of the whatever expression for the intensity pdf is deemed appropriate for the situation at hand.

4.3.2 Shack-Hartmann Model. The Shack-Hartmann model generated spot patterns by applying a lenslet-array phase delay to the simulated optical fields and then performing a numerical Fresnel propagation over a distance equal to the focal length of the lenslets. The lenslets were square, and side lengths d were chosen to be 1/16 the length of the observation region of interest, which were selected to achieve the desired value of d/r_0, *e.g* for $r_0 = 7.5$cm, a full aperture size $D = 1.2$m with 16 subapertures across resulted in $d/r_0 = 1$, while $D = 30$cm resulted in $d/r_0 = 1/4$. When the lenslets and their corresponding detector-array regions are the same size, the lenslet focal length can be computed by

$$f_\ell = \frac{n_s d^2}{n_p \lambda},\tag{135}$$

where n_s is the number of pixels per diffraction-limited half-spot, and n_p is the number of pixels across a subaperture side. The values for n_s and n_p were chosen to minimize their contribution to centroid error based on previous work presented in [41] and [91], and the focal length of the lenslets was selected for the different values of d/r_0 using Eq.(135). Winick derived the Cramer-Rao lower bound for centroid error as a function of pixel size relative to the size of a Gaussian spot on an infinite detector, which is effectively characterized by n_s [91]. However, for a diffraction-limited spot on a finite detector, Irwan and Lane showed in [41] that centroid error grows with detector array size and is also impacted by truncation error if the detector array is too small relative to the spot size. Based on their work, eight pixels/subaperture was chosen as the value for n_p, which ensured the detector integration area was sufficiently larger than the spot to avoid significant truncation error given the amount of tilt variance computed for the simulated optical fields.

4.3.3 Centroid-Error Variance Model. The model for centroid-error variance was implemented using Eq. (125). The scintillation index used in the model was that computed from the wave-optics observation fields, since scintillation metrics from wave-optics simulations have been shown to match experimental data better than theory [25]. A sinc^2 function was used for the spot shape and was numerically integrated over the pixels using adaptive Simpson quadrature. This step of numerically integrating the spot function over the pixels produces much more accurate results when spots are spread over a small number of pixels than closed-form expressions developed by integrating an analytical spot function over the pixel area. The value for K was set to the average number of photons/subaperture used to set the photon levels of the Shack-Hartmann spots.

4.3.4 Simulation Results. The metric for the wave-optics simulation results was the square root of the variance of the centroid error defined in Eq. (110). The simulation results were compared with the model for centroid-error variance by plotting the square root of the computed centroid-error variances. Figures 27 through 30 show results for $d/r_0 = 1$, $1/2$, and $1/4$ for 50, 200, 800, and 3200 photons per subaperture. In Fig. 27, centroid error is plotted versus photon level for the case of no scintillation; the blue markers show data from the simulation results, and the dashed, red lines show the predictions from the model. The lines showing the model predictions are not labeled since it is well understood that centroid error decreases with decreasing d/r_0. This figure shows that the best match between the model and the simulations occurs for $d/r_0 = 1/2$ and that the model slightly under-predicts centroid centroid error for smaller values of d/r_0 and slightly over-predicts centroid error for larger values of d/r_0. This may indicate that the spot shape has less impact on centroid error than expected. Ultimately, the data shows that, in the absence of scintillation and for $d/r_0 \leq 1$, the subaperture size does not significantly impact centroid error. Also,

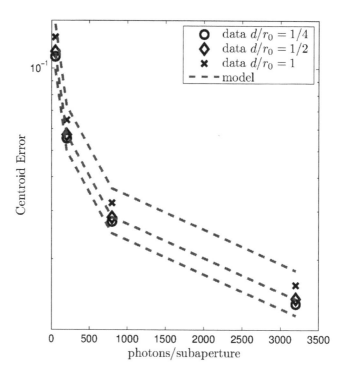

Figure 27:   Centroid-error Vs. photon level, no scintillation

the deviation of the model from the simulation results is small, and the model still captures the trend of decreasing centroid error with decreasing d/r_0.

In Figs. 28, through 30, centroid error is plotted as a function of Rytov number; the gray lines show the wave-optics results, and the dashed black lines show the prediction of the model given by the square root of Eq. (125). At the higher photon levels, the model matches the simulation outcomes well. As the photocounts decrease, the simulation results begin to deviate from the model slightly. However, the model matches the wave-optics simulation results well enough to provide reasonable predictions for centroid-error variance over a range of values for d/r_0, number of photons, and the scintillation index. Also, there is slightly better agreement between the $d/r_0 = 1$ results and the model than there is for the $d/r_0 = 1/2$ and $d/r_0 = 1/4$ cases. As discussed in Secs. 4.3.1 and 4.2.1, the discrepancy at smaller values of d/r_0

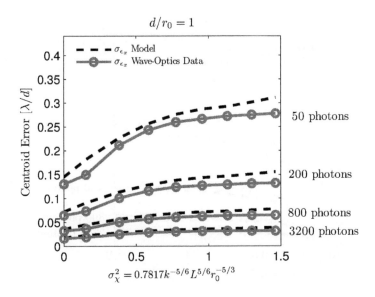

Figure 28:   Centroid-error simulation results for $d/r_0 = 1$

is likely due to the poorer agreement between the intensity pdf of the simulation data and the lognormal pdf assumed in deriving Eq. (125). However, there is reasonable agreement between the model and the simulation results for all cases of d/r_0, and the model does a good job of predicting the trends of the centroid error associated with photon noise in the presence of scintillation. Furthermore, obtaining agreement of probability densities for intensity in simulations, experiment, and theory is an active area of research. The model presented in Eq. (120) is general enough to allow the centroid-error variance to be modeled for a variety of intensity pdf's.

Figure 31 shows the model and wave-optics results for centroid-error σ_{ϵ_x} along with the full centroid error σ_{c_x} from the simulation for the lowest photon level at $d/r_0 = 1/4$. This shows that the centroid error due to scintillation and photon noise can make up a significant portion of the overall centroid error. The model provides a way of evaluating the design parameter space to ensure such error remains below an acceptable level.

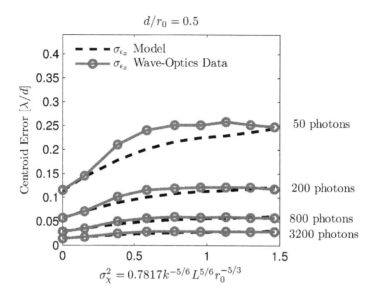

Figure 29:   Centroid-error simulation results for $d/r_0 = 1/2$

4.4   Conclusion

A very useful model has been presented for centroid error due to shot noise and scintillation. When scintillation is absent, the model reduces to the standard model assumed for photon noise only. Also, for subaperture sizes smaller than the atmospheric coherence width, the model can be adjusted to account for aberrations caused by the atmosphere. The model matches results of wave-optics simulations reasonably well. If enough light is available, the centroid-error variance due to scintillation and photon noise becomes relatively insensitive to scintillation. However, at low light levels, it is significantly impacted by scintillation in the weak regime. Also, at low light levels in small subapertures relative to r_0, the centroid-error variance becomes a significant part of the overall centroid variance.

The model is presented in a general form for any shape of intensity distribution and can be evaluated by numerically integrating over a complicated shape function or by assuming a simple shape function to attain more analytical solutions. Previously developed models that assumed constant intensity can be adjusted to account for

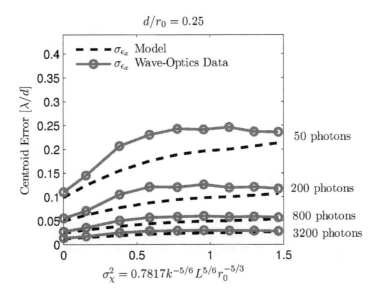

Figure 30: Centroid-error simulation results for $d/r_0 = 1/4$

scintillation using the model presented here. Finally, the presented model of centroid-error variance could be developed further by recognizing it as a conditional centroid variance and applying the conditional centroid variance formula to examine the impact of factors such as random centroid displacement and spot size.

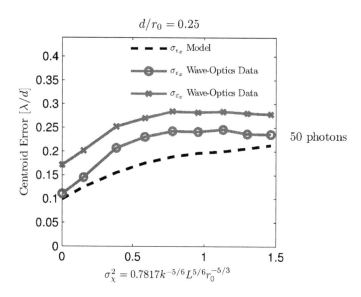

Figure 31:   Full centroid-error simulation results
Noise-induced centroid error σ_{ϵ_x} can be a significant portion of full-centroid error σ_{c_x}.

V. A Model for Shot-Noise-Induced Phase Error in SRI Measurements

5.1 Introduction

Adaptive optics systems correct optical distortions caused by propagation of light through a turbulent atmosphere. AO can greatly improve image quality in ground-based astronomical telescopes, significantly decrease bit-error rates in free-space optical communication, and enable beam-projection applications over long distances or through strong turbulence. Historically, the choice of WFS in an AO system has been heavily influenced by the intended application's operating conditions. For example, the strongest atmospheric turbulence is concentrated in a relatively thin layer near sea level, and wavefront distortions are relatively weak when they do not have long propagation paths over which to accumulate large phase deviations. In such conditions, scintillation, which is the occurence of random amplitude fluctuations in the received optical field, can largely be neglected. However, when the path between the source and receiver occurs over large volumes of constant turbulence strength, scintillation causes problems for traditional WFS's such as the Shack-Hartmann WFS and can severely limit the effectiveness of AO correction [5]. Also, many AO systems use an artificial beacon with quasi-monochromatic light, which enables coherent wavefront sensing. The SH WFS's poor performance in strong turbulence and the availability of a powerful, narrow-band beacon motivated the development of the SRI. The SRI is a relatively new approach to wavefront sensing that promises to extend AO operating regimes beyond weak fluctuations of the propagation medium and potentially provide drastic performance improvement in optical systems operating over long, horizontal propagation paths [63].

Measurements from an SRI can be mathematically formulated as the subaperture-averaged input optical field. SRI measurements therefore derive their statistical behavior from the mutual coherence function (MCF) with $\tau = 0$ (see Sec.2.2), which is referred to as the coherence factor. According to strong-turbulence theory, the MCF is independent of the scintillation index, so the formulation error of SRI measurements

115

was hypothesized to be insensitive to scintillation [6]. Wave-optics simulations have shown that the formulation error, characterized by the field-estimation Strehl ratio, is indeed insensitive to scintillation and therefore performs much better in strong, constant-strength turbulence than the SH or LSI WFS's [3].

However, AO systems that use a single deformable mirror (DM) to correct only phase distortions in the incident field rely on the WFS's ability to estimate optical phase, and the field-estimation Strehl ratio no longer fully characterizes the losses due to WFS estimation errors. The bulk of previously published work on SRI performance has used the field-estimation Strehl ratio, which only accounts for formulation error [3, 6, 63, 64]. Until now, SRI performance metrics that account for more than just formulation error have not been used, so the theoretical performance limitations associated with SRI estimation error have not been fully investigated. In fact, despite analytical predictions to the contrary, laboratory experiments implementing a single DM commanded by an SRI, which inherently include all sources of estimation error, have shown that the SRI's performance shows some sensitivity to scintillation [18].

In an effort to advance understanding of the SRI's performance limitations, this chapter provides an analytical model for the shot-noise-induced error variance of phase estimates computed from SRI measurements. The model is tested against both Monte Carlo and wave-optics simulations and is shown to agree reasonably well over a fairly wide range of atmospheric conditions. The model also predicts the dependence of SRI estimation error on scintillation, which, as previously mentioned, has been observed in laboratory experiments.

5.2 Derivation of SRI Photon-Noise-Induced Phase Error

The self-referencing interferometer (SRI) estimates an incident optical field from interferograms created by interfering replicas of the incident field with phase-shifted plane-wave reference beams. Figure 32 shows a diagram of a four-bin, spatial phase-shifting SRI. The incident optical field is split between a signal leg and a reference leg. Let β represent the fraction of power sent to the signal leg so that the signal field

116

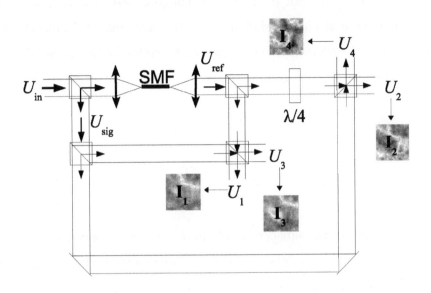

Figure 32:   Four-bin phase-shifting SRI
Illustration adapted from Fig. 2(a) in Ref. [64]. The reference beam U_{ref} is split and recombined with four samples of the signal beam U_{sig}, producing interfered fields U_1 through U_4. Interferograms I_1 through I_4 are the resulting irradiance patterns from recording U_1 through U_4 with photodetector arrays.

can be written as

$$U_{\text{sig}}(x, y) = \sqrt{\beta} U_{\text{in}}(x, y). \tag{136}$$

The portion of the input field sent to the reference leg is coupled into a single-mode fiber with coupling efficiency η_c and recollimated to form a plane-wave reference beam with $\xi = \eta_c(1 - \beta)$ times the power of the input field. The reference field is assumed to have amplitude uniformly distributed throughout the pupil and zero phase. Therefore the reference can be written as

$$U_{\text{ref}} = \left[\frac{\xi}{\mathcal{A}} \iint_{\mathcal{A}} |U_{\text{in}}(x, y)|^2 \mathrm{d}x\mathrm{d}y \right]^{1/2}, \tag{137}$$

where $\mathcal{A}$ is the area of the exit pupil of the collimating lens. The reference is split among four bins, each of which is shifted by $\theta = 0, \pi/2, \pi$, and $3\pi/2$ radians, respectively, before being interfered with equal-amplitude replicas of the signal beam. The phase-shift-dependent interferogram irradiance at the ith subaperture is given by

$$
\begin{aligned}
I(\theta) &= \frac{1}{4\mathcal{A}_i} \iint\limits_{\mathcal{A}_i} |U_{\text{sig}}(x,y) + U_{\text{ref}}\, e^{-j\theta}|^2 \mathrm{d}x\mathrm{d}y \\
&= \frac{1}{4}I_{\text{in}}\left\{ \beta + \xi + 2\sqrt{\beta\xi}\frac{1}{\mathcal{A}_i}\iint\limits_{\mathcal{A}_i} \cos[\phi(x,y) + \theta]\mathrm{d}x\mathrm{d}y \right\},
\end{aligned} \tag{138}
$$

where $\mathcal{A}_i$ is the area of the subaperture of interest and I_{in} is understood to be the irradiance of the input beam integrated over the area corresponding to the ith subaperture. The resulting interferograms are recorded by a photodector array. For irradiance that is uniform over the extent of a subaperture and for the duration of an integration time τ [s], the mean photocount is related to irradiance by

$$
\langle K \rangle = \alpha\tau\mathcal{A}_i I, \tag{139}
$$

where α is a factor that converts optical energy [J] to photons. This factor is given by

$$
\alpha = \frac{\eta_q}{hc/\lambda}, \tag{140}
$$

where $\eta_q \leq 1$ is the detector quantum efficiency, h is Planck's constant [6.626196×10^{-34} J·sec], c is the speed of light in vacuum [$\approx 2.998 \times 10^8$ m/sec], and λ is the optical wavelength [m].

To decrease hardware cost and complexity, the interfered beams of the four separate bins are often optically directed to a single photodector array as illustrated in Fig. 33 [63]. The average photocount of each bin of a single subaperture can be

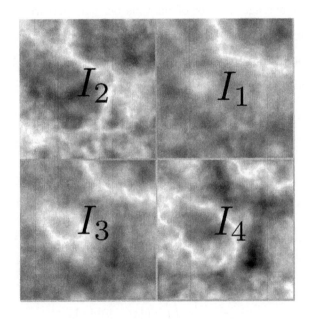

Figure 33:   Example of SRI interferograms

written as

$$\langle K_1 \rangle = \frac{1}{4}\langle K_{\text{in}} \rangle \left(\beta + \xi + 2\sqrt{\beta\xi}f \right)$$

$$\langle K_2 \rangle = \frac{1}{4}\langle K_{\text{in}} \rangle \left(\beta + \xi - 2\sqrt{\beta\xi}g \right)$$

$$\langle K_3 \rangle = \frac{1}{4}\langle K_{\text{in}} \rangle \left(\beta + \xi - 2\sqrt{\beta\xi}f \right)$$

$$\langle K_4 \rangle = \frac{1}{4}\langle K_{\text{in}} \rangle \left(\beta + \xi + 2\sqrt{\beta\xi}g \right), \tag{141}$$

where $\langle K_{\text{in}} \rangle$ is the average number of photons per subaperture in the incident optical field, and the functions f and g represent the subaperture-averaged, amplitude-normalized real and imaginary parts of the incident optical field. Explicitly, for a subaperture with location and area given by $\mathcal{A}_i$,

$$f \triangleq \frac{1}{\mathcal{A}_i} \iint_{\mathcal{A}_i} \frac{\Re\left[U_{\text{in}}(x,y)\right]}{|U_{\text{in}}(x,y)|} \mathrm{d}x\mathrm{d}y$$

$$= \frac{1}{\mathcal{A}_i} \iint_{\mathcal{A}_i} \cos[\phi(x,y)]\mathrm{d}x\mathrm{d}y; \tag{142}$$

$$g \triangleq \frac{1}{\mathcal{A}_i} \iint_{\mathcal{A}_i} \frac{\Im\left[U_{\text{in}}(x,y)\right]}{|U_{\text{in}}(x,y)|} \mathrm{d}x\mathrm{d}y$$

$$= \frac{1}{\mathcal{A}_i} \iint_{\mathcal{A}_i} \sin[\phi(x,y)]\mathrm{d}x\mathrm{d}y. \tag{143}$$

Because the SRI interferograms are proportional to the real and imaginary parts of the incident optical field, the subaperture-averaged field can be estimated as

$$\langle \hat{U} \rangle = \sqrt{\beta\xi}\,\langle K_{\text{in}} \rangle \left[\langle K_1 \rangle - \langle K_3 \rangle + \mathrm{j}\left(\langle K_4 \rangle - \langle K_2 \rangle \right) \right]. \tag{144}$$

The SRI field estimate has been shown to have a formulation error that depends only on the ratio of subaperture size d to atmospheric coherence width r_0 and is invariant with the strength of scintillation for a fixed value of d/r_0 [6]. However,

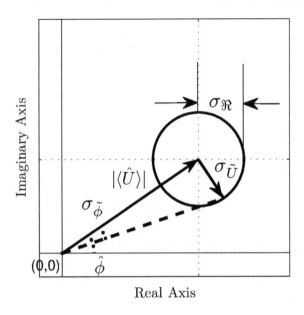

Figure 34:   SRI measurements on the complex plain

AO systems generally require phase estimates to correct optical turbulence with a deformable mirror (DM). Estimating the phase requires the use of transcendental functions, which complicates the noise analysis considerably. Following an approach similar to that used by Servin $et.\,al.$ in Sec. 5 of [44], an expression for noise-related phase error is developed with the assistance of a diagram of the SRI field estimate in the complex plane. This diagram, shown in Fig. 34, represents the SRI field estimate $\langle \hat{U} \rangle$ as a complex phasor with real and imaginary parts given by $\langle K_1 \rangle - \langle K_3 \rangle$ and $\langle K_4 \rangle - \langle K_2 \rangle$, respectively. Field estimates from SRI-interferogram photocounts are randomly distributed around the average value of the field estimate with a standard deviation $\sigma_{\tilde{U}}$. Since the four interferograms are recorded by different photodector arrays, the photon noise between bins is independent, and the noise of the real and imaginary parts of the estimate are equal. Therefore, $\sigma_{\tilde{U}}$ can be represented as the radius of a circle enclosing the region of greatest probability for the location of random field estimates. In Fig. 34, the radius is shown as being equal to the error of the real part of the phasor estimate $\sigma_{\Re}$. When the radius is directed so that it is tangent to the phasor estimate, the angular measurement error is given by

$$\sigma_{\hat{\phi}} = \tan^{-1}\left(\frac{\sigma_{\Re}}{|\langle\hat{U}\rangle|}\right). \tag{145}$$

Because we are only concerned with measurement error due to photon noise in the interferograms, $\sigma_{\Re}$ is understood to represent the deviation of the real part of the field estimate due only to photon noise, which can be written as

$$\sigma_{\Re} = \Delta K_1 - \Delta K_3, \tag{146}$$

where $\Delta K_1 \triangleq K_1 - \langle K_1\rangle$ and $\Delta K_3 \triangleq K_3 - \langle K_3\rangle$ are the fluctuations of photocounts about the means of the first and third bins due to photon noise and by definition have means equal to zero. The variance of the real part of the SRI estimate due to photon noise is given by

$$
\begin{aligned}
\sigma_{\Re}^2 &= \left\langle[(\Delta K_1 - \Delta K_3) - (\langle\Delta K_1\rangle - \langle\Delta K_3\rangle)]^2\right\rangle \\
&= \left\langle[(K_1 - \langle K_1\rangle) - (K_3 - \langle K_3\rangle)]^2\right\rangle \\
&= \left\langle(K_1 - \langle K_1\rangle)^2\right\rangle + \left\langle(K_3 - \langle K_3\rangle)^2\right\rangle - 2\left\langle(K_1 - \langle K_1\rangle)(K_3 - \langle K_3\rangle)\right\rangle \\
&= \sigma_{K_1}^2 + \sigma_{K_3}^2.
\end{aligned}
\tag{147}
$$

The phasor amplitude is given by

$$|\langle\hat{U}\rangle| = \sqrt{(\langle K_1\rangle - \langle K_3\rangle)^2 + (\langle K_4\rangle - \langle K_2\rangle)^2}. \tag{148}$$

Also, for Poisson-distributed photocounts, the photocount variance of each bin is equal to its respective mean photocount. Therefore, by substituting Eqs. (147) and (148) into Eq. (145) and using the definitions for the mean photocounts of the SRI bins given by Eq. (141), the residual-phase variance can be written as

$$
\begin{aligned}
\sigma_{\tilde\phi}^2 &= \left(\tan^{-1}\left\{\left[\frac{\langle K_1\rangle + \langle K_3\rangle}{(\langle K_1\rangle - \langle K_3\rangle)^2 + (\langle K_4\rangle - \langle K_2\rangle)^2}\right]^{1/2}\right\}\right)^2 \\
&= \left(\tan^{-1}\left\{\left[\frac{(\beta + \xi)}{2\langle K_{\mathrm{in}}\rangle\beta\xi(f^2 + g^2)}\right]^{1/2}\right\}\right)^2 .
\end{aligned}
$$

In the absence of scintillation and for small enough subapertures, $\langle K_{\mathrm{in}}\rangle$ and f can be assumed to be deterministic quantities, and the small-angle approximation can be used to reduce the expression for residual phase variance to

$$
\sigma_{\tilde\phi,\mathrm{small}}^2 = \frac{\beta + \xi}{2\langle K_{\mathrm{in}}\rangle\beta\xi(f^2 + g^2)}. \tag{149}
$$

However, if scintillation is present, or if the subapertures are large relative to r_0, the residual phase variance must be averaged over the statistics of irradiance and phase fluctuations that were not removed by subtracting off the least-squares-unwrapped noiseless phase. Toward this end, it is helpful to define $\tilde{f}$ and $\tilde{g}$ as the subaperture-averaged, amplitude-normalized real and imaginary parts of the SRI field estimate caused by photon noise, which can be expressed by substituting the SRI field-estimate fluctuations $\tilde{U}$ for U_{in} in Eqs. (142) and (143). The average over $\tilde{f}^2$ and $\tilde{g}^2$ can then be written as

$$
\begin{aligned}
\langle \tilde{f}^2 + \tilde{g}^2\rangle &= \left\langle\left\{\frac{1}{\mathcal{A}_i}\iint\limits_{\mathcal{A}_i}\frac{\Re\left[\tilde{U}(x,y)\right]}{|\tilde{U}(x,y)|}\,dxdy\right\}^2\right\rangle + \left\langle\left\{\frac{1}{\mathcal{A}_i}\iint\limits_{\mathcal{A}_i}\frac{\Im\left[\tilde{U}(x,y)\right]}{|\tilde{U}(x,y)|}\,dxdy\right\}^2\right\rangle \\
&= \frac{1}{\mathcal{A}_i^2}\iint\limits_{\mathcal{A}_i}\iint\limits_{\mathcal{A}_i}\left\langle\frac{\Re\left[\tilde{U}(\boldsymbol{r}_1)\right]\Re\left[\tilde{U}(\boldsymbol{r}_2)\right] + \Im\left[\tilde{U}(\boldsymbol{r}_1)\right]\Im\left[\tilde{U}(\boldsymbol{r}_2)\right]}{\left[|\tilde{U}(\boldsymbol{r}_1)|^2|\tilde{U}(\boldsymbol{r}_2)|^2\right]^{1/2}}\right\rangle d\boldsymbol{r}_1 d\boldsymbol{r}_2,
\end{aligned}
$$

$$\tag{150}$$

where $\boldsymbol{r}_1 = (x_1, y_1)$ and $\boldsymbol{r}_2 = (x_2, y_2)$ are radial coordinate vectors inside the ith subaperture. A bit of algebra applied to this expression reveals that $\langle \tilde{f}^2 + \tilde{g}^2\rangle$ is the subaperture-averaged coherence factor μ_{12} [see Eq. (33) in Sec. 2.2] of a homogeneous and isotropic field [34].

Since Monte Carlo simulations showed that the residual phase variance is too large to justify the small-angle approximation, the treatment of random irradiance begins with the argument of the inverse tangent function in Eq. (149). As long as the irradiance remains uniform over the extent of a subaperture, random irradiance from subaperture-to-subaperture or between realizations does not increase the phase variance as long as there is a large enough signal-to-noise ratio (SNR). This is easily explained by referring to Fig. 34 and noting that an increase in irradiance, which corresponds to an increase in the amplitude of the field-estimate phasor, does not change the phase of the estimate. So, at high SNR's where the radius of the noise circle is sufficiently smaller than the amplitude of the estimate, any phase variance due to random irradiance fluctuations is negligible. However, when random irradiance fluctuations are coupled with photon noise at low light levels, the phase estimate does suffer an increase in phase variance. An estimate for this effect begins by averaging the argument of the inverse tangent function of Eq. (149) over the probability distribution function (pdf) of the irradiance fluctuations. To simplify the analysis, we still assume that irradiance fluctuations remain constant at least over the extent of a subaperture and the duration of an integration time. Also, as discussed in Sec. 4.2, for the subaperture sizes of interest in this work ($d/r_0 \leq 1$), scintillation aperture-averaging effects are negligible, and the intensity is essentially constant over the extent of a subaperture, $i.e.$ subapertures behave as point receivers [1]. Therefore, the desired average over the pdf of irradiance $p_I(I)$ can be written as

$$
\begin{aligned}
\langle \arg(\sigma_{\hat{\phi}}) \rangle_{I_{\text{in}}} &= \left\langle \left[\frac{(\beta + \xi)}{2\langle K_{\text{in}} \rangle \beta \xi \mu_{12}} \right]^{1/2} \right\rangle_{I_{\text{in}}} \\
&= \left[\frac{(\beta + \xi)}{2\alpha\tau\mathcal{A}_i\beta\xi\mu_{12}} \right]^{1/2} \int_0^\infty \frac{1}{\sqrt{I_{\text{in}}}} p_I(I) \mathrm{d}I.
\end{aligned}
\tag{151}
$$

For light with phase and amplitude fluctuations caused by atmospheric turbulence, the classical irradiance fluctuations follow a log-normal distribution under the first-order Rytov approximation [1]. The log-normal pdf of irradiance is given by

$$p_I(I) = \frac{1}{I\sigma\sqrt{2\pi}} \exp\left[\frac{-(\ln I - \mu)^2}{2\sigma^2}\right], \tag{152}$$

where μ and σ are parameters related to the irradiance mean $\langle I \rangle$ and variance σ_I^2 by Eqs. (122) and (123) in Sec. 4.2. Also, as in Sec. 4.2, the log-normal-pdf parameters μ and σ are expressed in terms of the scintillation index defined by Eq. (124). Substituting the log-normal pdf into Eq. (151) and evaluating the integral leads to the irradiance-averaged argument of the residual phase variance

$$\langle \arg(\sigma_{\tilde\phi}) \rangle_{I_{\text{in}}} = \left[\frac{(\beta+\xi)}{2\alpha\tau\mathcal{A}_i\beta\xi\mu_{12}}\right]^{1/2} \frac{(\tilde\sigma_I^2+1)^{3/8}}{\sqrt{\langle I_{\text{in}}\rangle}}$$

$$= \left[\frac{(\beta+\xi)}{2\langle\langle K_{\text{in}}\rangle_I\rangle_K\beta\xi\mu_{12}}\right]^{1/2} (\tilde\sigma_I^2+1)^{3/8}, \tag{153}$$

where $\langle\langle K_{\text{in}}\rangle_I\rangle_K$ indicates the irradiance-averaged average photocount of the subaperture input. Substituting Eq. (153) into Eq. (149) provides the expression for the shot-noise-induced residual phase variance that accounts for the effects of scintillation

$$\sigma_{\tilde\phi}^2 = \left(\tan^{-1}\left\{\left[\frac{(\beta+\xi)}{2\langle\langle K_{\text{in}}\rangle_I\rangle_K\beta\xi\mu_{12}}\right]^{1/2} (\tilde\sigma_I^2+1)^{3/8}\right\}\right)^2. \tag{154}$$

Equation (154) is the key result of this chapter.

It is important to emphasize that this model started from the assumption of lognormally-distibuted irradiance. However, other pdf's of irradiance have been proposed that may, in certain circumstances, describe the irradiance pdf better than the lognormal distribution. The gamma-gamma pdf described in Ch. IV is a good example. The choice of irradiance pdf could have a significant impact on the model for phase-error variance for the same reasons it has a significant impact on centroid-error variance as discussed in Sec. 4.2.1.

125

5.3 Monte Carlo Simulations

Monte Carlo simulations are often used to study the impact of noise on WFS measurements [32, 79]. The simulations referred to in this chapter as Monte Carlo simulations did not involve wave-optics propagation. Instead, the simulated fields were formed from separately-generated irradiance profiles and atmospheric phase screens. A single value of r_0 was used to generate a number of realizations of phase screens over a range of subaperture sizes for three different sizes of the full-aperture. Optical fields without scintillation were generated by forming complex fields with uniform amplitude and phase given by the phase screens. Scintillation effects were implemented by using a random number generator to produce lognormally-distributed irradiance profiles with the desired average number of photons per subaperture as well as the desired scintillation index. The simulated optical fields were then used to generate the four SRI interferograms, which were averaged over the subapertures and then passed as the parameter to a Poisson-random-variable generator to simulate photon noise. The splitting parameters β and ξ were each set equal to 1/2. The field was estimated using Eq. (144), and the phase estimate was computed using the four-quadrant, inverse tangent of the imaginary and real parts of the field estimate. The phase estimate was then unwrapped using a least-squares phase-unwrapping algorithm, and the aperture-averaged phase (piston) was subtracted from each realization. The noise-induced phase-estimation error was then computed by subtracting the piston-removed least-squares-unwrapped phase ϕ of the subaperture-averaged input optical field from the SRI phase estimate. The variance of the resulting residual phase was computed from all subapertures in all realizations for each case of d/r_0, D/r_0, and input number of photons per subaperture.

The Monte Carlo simulations showed that the residual phase variance is a function of subaperture size characterized by d/r_0, full-aperture size D/r_0, and the total number of incident photons. Figures 35 and 36 show results that suggest a dependence of the coherence factor μ_{12} on both d/r_0 and D/r_0. The figures plot the mean subaperture photocounts of the SRI bins (a) and the variance of the subaperture

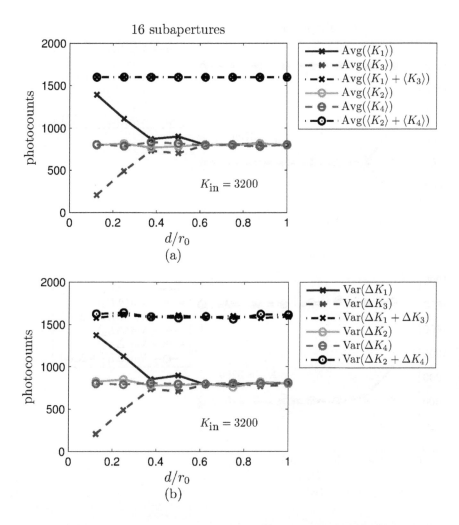

Figure 35:   SRI Monte Carlo photocount variance, 16^2 subapertures
Average bin photocounts and photon-noise variance computed from SRI Monte Carlo simulations for 16 subapertures per full-aperture side length D and 3200 photons/-subaperture.

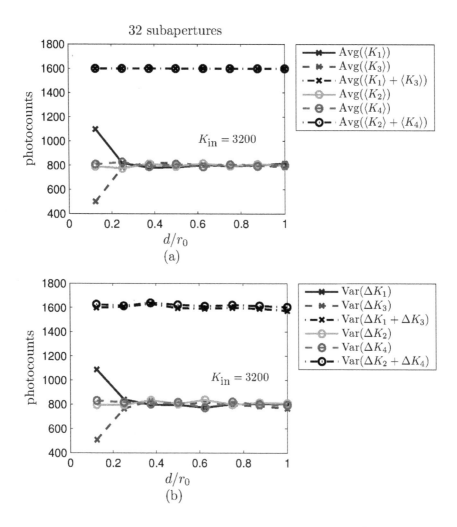

Figure 36:   SRI Monte Carlo photocount variance, 32^2 subapertures
Average bin photocounts and photon-noise variance computed from SRI Monte Carlo simulations for 32 subapertures per full-aperture side length D and 3200 photons/-subaperture.

photon noise (b). Figure 35 shows the results for the case of 16 subapertures and 3200 photons, and Fig. 36 shows the results for 32 subapertures and 3200 photons. Comparing plots (a) with plots (b) in the figures verifies that the variances of ΔK are equal to the mean photocounts and that the bin photocounts of the real and imaginary parts sum to the appropriate values. These plots also show an interesting trend in the photocounts of the first and third bins. Because the input phase has a mean of zero, the expected value of f is 1. However, as d/r_0 increases, the mean of subaperture photocounts of the first bin decreases from its expected value of half the total number of input photons per subaperture (when $\beta = \xi = 1/2$). Similarly, the third bin increases from its expected value of zero. In both cases of 16 and 32 subapertures across the pupil, the values of the bin photocounts asymptotically approach 800, which is one fourth the total number of input photons. This would be expected if f were equal to zero and $\beta = \xi$ [see Eq. (141)]. The diminishing impact of the phase term in the first- and third-bin photocounts seems to indicate that the depth of modulation is decreasing as d/r_0 increases. The decrease in modulation depth shown here is due to photon noise. Also, in Fig. 35 this decrease in modulation depth for the case of 16 subapertures/D appears to be less significant than that suggested by Fig. 36 for the case of 32 subapertures/D. Since the same subaperture size was used for each of these cases, the full-aperture size D was different for each case. Therefore, the modulation depth appears to also be a function of the full aperture size characterized by D/r_0. This may be due to the aperture-averaged phase variance that increases as $(D/r_0)^{5/3}$ [71].

The impact of subaperture size on residual-phase-variance, or sampling error, from the Monte Carlo simulations is shown in Figs. 37 and 38 for the cases of 50 and 200 photons per subaperture, respectively. First, these results show that at larger values of d/r_0 the residual phase variance becomes too large to justify the small angle approximation. However, substituting the square root of Eq. (149) as the argument of the inverse tangent function in Eq. (149) results in a reasonably close fit to the data when an appropriate function is used for μ_{12}. The simulations also show that the

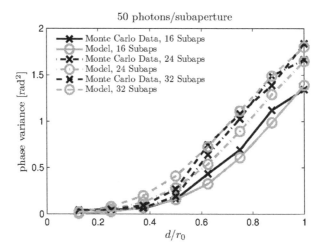

Figure 37: SRI sampling error (Monte Carlo), 50 phot./subap. Photon-noise-induced phase-error variance computed from SRI Monte Carlo simulations for 50 photons/subaperture.

residual phase variance depends on the number of subapertures, which corresponds to a larger full-aperture size characterized by D/r_0.

Therefore, an expression for the coherence factor was formed by multiplying the usual expression for the coherence factor $\exp\left[-3.44(d/r_0)^{5/3}\right]$ by a factor that includes the D/r_0 dependence observed in the Monte Carlo data. The expression for the coherence factor found to provide the closest match of the residual-phase-variance model to the Monte Carlo simulation results is

$$\mu_{12} = \exp\left[-3.44\left(\frac{d}{r_0}\right)^{5/3}\right]\left(0.1578 \cdot \frac{D}{r_0}\right)^{-5/3}. \qquad (155)$$

The constant factor 0.1578 was determined from surface fits to the phase variance computed from Monte Carlo simulations over a range of parameters. Table 1 shows the values of the surface-fit parameter a for each case of the number of input photons per subaperture. The surfaces were fit to the Monte Carlo residual-phase-variance values plotted as a function of d/r_0 and D/r_0. Eight equally-spaced values of d/r_0 ranging from 1/8 to 1 were used, and the values used for the number of subapertures/D were

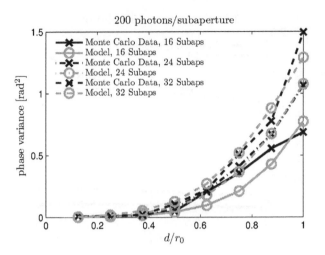

Figure 38: SRI sampling error (Monte Carlo), 200 phot./subap. Photon-noise-induced phase variance computed from SRI Monte Carlo simulations for 200 photons/subaperture.

Table 1: Residual-Phase-Variance Fitting Parameter

*	50 photons	200 photons	800 photons	3200 photons
a	0.1620	0.1553	0.1704	0.2005
CI	(0.1497,0.1743)	(0.1444,0.1661)	(0.1577,0.1831)	(0.1796,0.2214)
r^2	0.9683	0.9510	0.9090	0.7467
rmse	0.11620	0.08675	0.06458	0.05271

*a is the fitting parameter, CI is the 95% confidence-interval bounds, r^2 is the coefficient of determination, and rmse is the root-mean-square error of the fit.

12, 16, 24, 32, and 48. The value 0.1578 for the constant factor in Eq. (155) is the offset (y-intercept) of a least-squares fit of a line to the values of the surface-fit parameter a shown in Table 1. While there appears to be a slight dependence of a on the number of photons, the slope of the fit line was 1.3×10^{-5}, so this dependence was neglected. This apparent dependence most likely has more to do with the fact that Eq. (155) provides a poorer fit to the data as the number of photons per subaperture increases, which is evidenced by the corresponding decrease in the coefficient of determination r^2, also shown in the table.

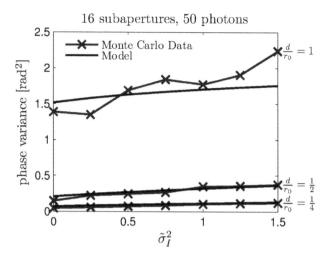

Figure 39: SRI phase-error variance (Monte Carlo), 50 photons, $d = D/16$
Photon-noise-induced phase variance as a function of scintillation strength from SRI
Monte Carlo simulations for 16 subapertures/D 50 photons/subaperture.

The model for the residual-phase variance was computed by substituting Eq. (155)
for μ_{12} in Eq. (154). Plots of the residual phase variance are shown in Figs. 39 through
42. These plots show the variance as a function of scintillation index since the scintillated irradiance profiles were generated directly from arbitrarily-chosen values of the
scintillation index. Also, the values of scintillation index used in the Monte Carlo simulations correspond to values of log-amplitude variance ranging from 0 to 0.25, which
represents the weak-scintillation regime [1, 71]. Figures 39 and 40 show the phase-
error variance from the Monte Carlo simulations for 16×16 subapertures with 50 and
200 photons per subaperture, respectively. Figures 41 and 42 show the phase-error
variance for 50 and 200 photons with 32×32 subapertures. The model provides a
reasonable (and very useful) prediction for the residual phase variance in the presence
of scintillation that can be modeled as log-normally distributed subaperture-photon
levels. Figures 39 and 41 show that the agreement is particularly close for low illumination.

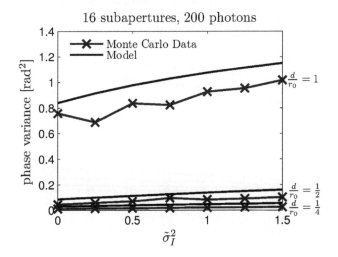

Figure 40:   SRI phase-error variance (Monte Carlo), 200 photons, $d = D/16$
Photon-noise-induced phase variance as a function of scintillation strength from SRI
Monte Carlo simulations for 16 subapertures/D and 200 photons/subaperture.

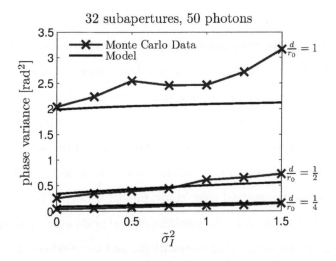

Figure 41:   SRI phase-error variance (Monte Carlo), 50 photons, $d = D/32$
Photon-noise-induced phase variance as a function of scintillation strength from SRI
Monte Carlo simulations for 32 subapertures/D and 50 photons/subaperture.

133

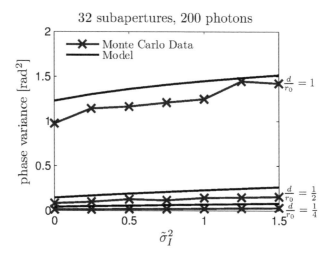

Figure 42: SRI phase-error variance (Monte Carlo), 200 photons, $d = D/32$
Photon-noise-induced phase variance as a function of scintillation strength from SRI
Monte Carlo simulations for 32 subapertures/D and 200 photons/subaperture.

5.4 Testing the Model against Wave-Optics Simulations

Wave-optics simulations provide a slightly better test of how well a model represents physical reality. Also, they have been preferred for testing WFS performance
when beacons are scintillated by propagation through volume-distributed atmospheric
turbulence [3–5]. To test the model presented here, optical fields were generated by
numerically propagating an on-axis point source through 40 atmospheric realizations,
each modeled by ten Kolmogorov phase screens. The phase screens were evenly spaced
throughout the propagation path and designed to provide a total-path, spherical-wave
atmospheric coherence width of $r_0 = 7.5$cm. Since the same simulated optical fields
were used here as for the centroid-error study, further details on the wave-optics simulations can be found in Sec. 4.3. The resulting optical fields were then sent to the same
SRI model used for the Monte Carlo simulations, and the residual phase variance was
computed in the same way described in Sec. 5.3.

The model was computed in the same way as described for the Monte Carlo
simulations, except that $\tilde{\sigma}_I^2$ was computed according to its definition in Eq. (124)

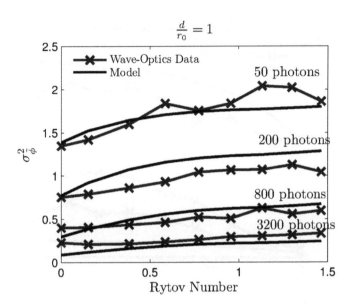

Figure 43: SRI phase-error variance (wave-optics), $d = D/16$, $d/r_0 = 1$
SRI photon-noise-induced phase variance computed from wave-optics simulations plotted as a function of scintillation strength characterized by Rytov number.

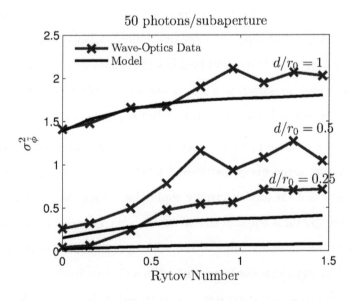

Figure 44: SRI phase-error variance (wave-optics), 50 photons, $d = D/16$
SRI photon-noise-induced phase variance computed from wave-optics simulations plotted as a function of scintillation strength characterized by Rytov number.

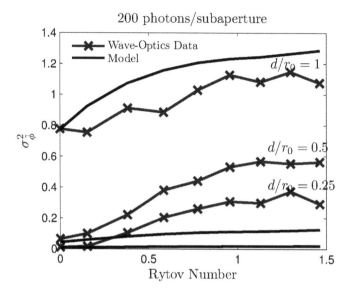

Figure 45: SRI phase-error variance (wave-optics), 200 photons, $d = D/16$
SRI photon-noise-induced phase variance computed from wave-optics simulations
plotted as a function of scintillation strength characterized by Rytov number.

from the variance and squared mean of the irradiance of the 40 realizations of 256×256 input fields. Figure 43 shows the residual phase variance from the wave-optics simulations with $d/r_0 = 1$. The model matches the simulation results reasonably well for this case. However, as shown in Figs. 44 and 45, at values of $d/r_0 < 1$ the model underestimates the residual phase variance at Rytov numbers greater than about 0.2.

The model for residual phase variance in scintillation expressed by Eq. (154) was derived by assuming lognormally-distributed irradiance. The results in Figs. 44 and 45 seem to suggest that the model actually applies best when the scintillation has been averaged over subapertures equal in size to r_0. This is consistent with observations in Ch. IV regarding the intensity pdf's of the wave-optics simulation data. Figures 24 and 25 in Sec. 4.3.1 show that the lognormal pdf fits the intensity pdf of the simulation data less as subaperture size decreases. As discussed in Sec. 4.2.1, the assumed pdf has a significant impact on the integrand in the error-variance models that account for intensity fluctuations by averaging the conditional error variance over the intensity pdf.

5.5 Conclusion

A model for the shot-noise-induced residual phase variance has been derived that accounts for the effects of scintillation and, for the first time, predicts the experimentally observed dependence of SRI measurements on scintillation strength [63]. Monte Carlo simulations were used to evaluate and refine the model by accounting for complicated effects of subaperture and full-aperture sizes. The resulting model was then tested against wave-optics simulations, which showed reasonable agreement between the model and the simulations. This model accounts for phase-error variance in a four-bin, spatial-phase-shifting SRI due to photon noise and lognormally-distributed irradiance fluctuations. The method used here could lead to other models for phase-error variance for irradiance fluctuations that are not lognormally distributed, but they may require numerical integration. This model does not account for phase and irradiance fluctuations within a subaperture, which may account for some of the discrepancies between the model and the simulation. Additionally, the simulations did not realistically model fiber coupling in the reference leg of the SRI, and the model for residual phase variance did not attempt to account for errors associated with fiber coupling beyond the inclusion of the splitting parameters β and ξ. These issues were left as future work so that the present model could be used to design a hybrid WFS using the SRI and a SH WFS.

VI. Hybrid Wavefront Sensor

6.1 Introduction

The Shack-Hartmann wavefront sensor and the self-referencing interferometer are complementary sensors used to measure the phase of optical fields in adaptive-optics control systems. AO systems use the phase measurements from a WFS to command a deformable mirror for correcting wavefront distortions caused by system aberrations or random distortions such as the optical effects of atmospheric turbulence. The unique and complementary characteristics of the SH and SRI WFS's motivated this study of the potential for improving WFS performance by combining them into a hybrid WFS.

The Shack-Hartmann sensor estimates local wavefront slopes from intensity measurements at the focal plane of a lenslet array. The slope measurements can then be least-squares reconstructed into phase estimates for effective control of a DM in an AO system as long as there is sufficient signal-to-noise ratio and small enough subapertures to adequately sample the turbulence. However, scintillated optical fields can cause problems for SH-WFS slope measurements when SNR is low. In fact, the SH WFS's formulation error can be significant in strong scintillation due to low signal levels in the vicinity of branch points [3, 5, 29]. Despite its weaknesses in strong scintillation, the SH WFS has actually outperformed other WFS's in low scintillation strength [3]. Also, because the SH WFS uses focal-plane measurements and has low-resolution imaging capability, it is possible, within certain limitations, to form phase estimates even when the beacon has finite extent. Furthermore, the SH WFS's focal-plane imaging capability also enables it to use broadband sources as beacons. Finally, the SH WFS lends itself naturally to estimation of the least-squares phase of atmospheric turbulence because its measurements can be directly related to phase differences across its subapertures (*i.e.* wavefront slope).

The SRI uses phase-shifting interferometry to estimate the optical field in the pupil plane. These pupil-plane measurements provide estimates for the principal-value (*a.k.a.* modulo-2π or wrapped) phase that generally must be unwrapped to

138

command the actuators of a continuous-facesheet DM. Formulation error in the SRI has been shown to be insensitive to scintillation, which makes it a natural choice for improving AO performance in strong scintillation [3,6]. Wave-optics results reported by Barchers *et al.* confirmed this prediction and showed that the SRI outperformed a SH WFS in strong scintillation even when a branch-point-tolerant phase reconstructor was used for the SH measurements [3,6]. However, the same results also showed that in weak scintillation the SH WFS outperformed the SRI. Also, since the SRI relies on interferometry, it requires a narrow-band, point-source beacon to operate effectively and may be signifciantly challenged by extended beacons. Finally, because SRI phase estimates must be unwrapped to control a continuous-facesheet DM, least-squares phase reconstruction is required just as it is for the SH WFS.

Because of their complementary strengths and weaknesses, the SH and SRI sensors are reasonable choices for developing a hybrid WFS that can deal with a range of beacon characteristics and atmospheric conditions. Measurements from the SH and SRI WFS's also fit naturally into a least-squares and principal-value (LSPV) phase-unwrapping approach [52, 86]. This chapter proposes, models, and simulates a hybrid WFS that combines SH and SRI measurements to form phase estimates in a way that employs the strengths and mitigates the weaknesses of each individual WFS. The approach is based on semi-analytic models for the variances of SH and SRI phase measurements. These models have been shown in Chapters IV and V to agree reasonably well with wave-optics simulations. Under the assumption that lower phase variance should lead to better phase estimation and AO compensation, the models serve as tools for making critical design decisions that ensure optimum performance of each WFS on its own and suggest ways to combine them for further performance improvements. Based on the models of individual WFS phase variances, a maximum-likelihood, weighted-average hybrid WFS is developed that performs better at estimating the least-squares phase than a comparable stand-alone SRI in open-loop wave-optics simulations using a point-source beacon propagated through atmospheric turbulence. Further, the hybrid WFS is also shown to provide benefits over a comparable stand-alone SRI even when performing LSPV phase unwrapping to improve performance in the presence of branch points.

6.2 SRI Phase Variance Model

From Ch. V, a model for photon-noise-induced phase-error variance σ_{sri}^2 computed from field measurements made by a four-bin phase-shifting self-referencing interferometer (SRI) is given by

$$
\begin{aligned}
\sigma_{\text{sri}}^2 &= \left(\tan^{-1} \left\{ \left[\frac{(\beta + \xi)}{2 K_{\text{sri}} \beta \xi \mu_{12}} \right]^{1/2} \left(\tilde{\sigma}_I^2 + 1 \right)^{3/8} \right\} \right)^2 \\
&\approx \frac{(\beta + \xi)}{2 K_{\text{sri}} \beta \xi \mu_{12}} \left(\tilde{\sigma}_I^2 + 1 \right)^{3/4},
\end{aligned}
\tag{156}
$$

where K_{sri} is the mean number of available photons per subaperture, β is the fraction of power split to the signal leg of the SRI, ξ is the fraction of power split to the reference leg, μ_{12} is the spatial coherence factor of the beacon, and $\tilde{\sigma}_I^2$ is the scintillation index. The scintillation index is defined as

$$
\tilde{\sigma}_I^2 \triangleq \frac{\sigma_I^2}{\langle I \rangle^2},
\tag{157}
$$

where σ_I^2 is the irradiance variance and $\langle I \rangle$ is the mean irradiance. Also, the fraction of power split to the reference leg can be expressed in terms of the losses due to imperfect coupling efficiency η_c and the light split to the signal leg as

$$
\xi \triangleq \eta_c (1 - \beta).
\tag{158}
$$

140

Furthermore, the fringe visibility, or modulation depth, of the SRI interferograms can be expressed as (p.182 in [34])

$$
\begin{aligned}
\mathcal{V} &= \frac{2\sqrt{K_s K_r}}{K_s + K_r}\mu_{12} \\
&= \frac{2\sqrt{\beta\xi}}{\beta + \xi}\mu_{12},
\end{aligned}
\tag{159}
$$

where $K_s = \beta K_{\mathrm{sri}}$ is the mean number of photons per subaperture sent to the SRI's signal leg, and $K_r = \xi K_{\mathrm{sri}}$ is the number of photons per subaperture sent to the reference leg. It follows that the SRI phase variance can also be expressed in terms of the fringe visibility as

$$
\sigma_{\mathrm{sri}}^2 = \frac{1}{K_{\mathrm{sri}}\sqrt{\beta\xi}\,\mathcal{V}}\left(\tilde{\sigma}_I^2 + 1\right)^{3/4}.
\tag{160}
$$

The best fit to phase variance computed from Monte Carlo simulation data resulted when the fringe visibility was modeled as

$$
\mathcal{V} = \frac{2\sqrt{\beta\xi}}{\beta + \xi}\exp\left[-3.44\left(\frac{d}{r_0}\right)^{5/3}\right]\left(0.1578 \cdot \frac{D}{r_0}\right)^{-5/3}.
\tag{161}
$$

This resulted in a model for phase variance that agreeed well with wave-optics simulations over a range of atmospheric conditions characterized by d/r_0 and Rytov number.

6.3 Shack-Hartmann Phase Variance Model

From Ch. IV, a model for the variance σ_{sh}^2 of phase estimates reconstructed from Shack-Hartmann-centroid-based slope measurements is given by

$$
\sigma_{\mathrm{sh}}^2 = 2\frac{(2\pi)^2}{K_{\mathrm{sh}}}\sum_{i=1}^{N^2} x_i^2 f_i\left(\tilde{\sigma}_I^2 + 1\right),
\tag{162}
$$

where K_{sh} is the mean number of photons incident on each Shack-Hartmann lenslet (or subaperture), f_i is the fraction of light incident on the ith pixel of a subaperture's detector array, N is the number of pixels across the detector array, and $\tilde{\sigma}_I^2$ is the scintillation index defined in Eq. (157). The expression in Eq. (162) requires the subaperture pixel coordinates x_i to be expressed in normalized angular units where the factor of normalization is the diffraction angle λ/d [rad]. Equation (162) also assumes a linear calibration curve with a slope of one, and sets the reconstructor propagation error to unity, which is a close approximation for a large number of actuators and likely overestimates propagation error for tilt-removed phase [28, 50].

The Shack-Hartmann phase variance can be computed by numerically integrating over an assumed spot function, *i.e.* f_i can be written as

$$f_i = \iint_{\mathcal{A}_i} f(x, y, w) \mathrm{d}x \mathrm{d}y, \tag{163}$$

where $\mathcal{A}_i$ is the solid angle of the ith pixel, $f(x, y, w)$ is the assumed spot function, x and y are the coordinates inside a subaperture, and w is the width of the spot. For square subapertures, the spot function is given by

$$f(x, y, w) = \frac{1}{w^2} \mathrm{sinc}^2\left(\frac{x}{w}\right) \mathrm{sinc}^2\left(\frac{y}{w}\right), \tag{164}$$

where $\mathrm{sinc}(x) \triangleq \sin(\pi x)/(\pi x)$. To account for spreading of the spot due to atmospheric turbulence, an effective spot width can be defined in terms of the diffraction-limited spot width w_{DL}, the optical transfer function (OTF) of the lenslet $\mathcal{H}_{\mathrm{opt}}$, and the OTF of the atmosphere $\mathcal{H}_{\mathrm{atm}}$ as

$$w_{\mathrm{eff}} = w_{\mathrm{DL}} \times \left[\frac{\int\limits_{-\infty}^{\infty}\!\!\int \mathcal{H}_{\mathrm{opt}}(f_X, f_Y) \mathrm{d}f_X \mathrm{d}f_Y}{\int\limits_{-\infty}^{\infty}\!\!\int \mathcal{H}_{\mathrm{opt}}(f_X, f_Y) \mathcal{H}_{\mathrm{atm}}(f_X, f_Y) \mathrm{d}f_X \mathrm{d}f_Y} \right]^{1/2}, \tag{165}$$

where f_X and f_Y are spatial-frequency coordinates. For a square lenslet, the one-dimensional OTF of the optics is given by

$$\mathcal{H}_{\text{opt}}(f_X) = \Lambda\left(\frac{f_X}{2f_0}\right), \tag{166}$$

where $2f_0 = d/(\lambda f_\ell)$ is the spatial cutoff frequency [35]. The triangle function Λ is defined as

$$\Lambda(x) = \begin{cases} 1 - |x| & |x| \leq 1 \\ 0 & \text{otherwise.} \end{cases} \tag{167}$$

The short-exposure OTF of the atmosphere is defined as

$$\mathcal{H}_{\text{atm}}(\rho) = \exp\left\{-3.44\left(\frac{\rho}{r_0}\right)^{5/3}\left[1 - a\left(\frac{\rho}{d}\right)^{1/3}\right]\right\}, \tag{168}$$

where $\rho = (f_X^2 + f_Y^2)^{1/2}$ is a radial spatial frequency coordinate, and a is a scintillation parameter; $a = 1$ in the absence of scintillation, and $a = 1/2$ when scintillation is present [34]. Given a set of values for d, r_0, and a, the effective spot width w_{eff} can be computed by substituting Eqs. (166) and (168) into Eq. (165) and evaluating the integrals numerically. This effective spot width is then used in numerically evaluating the integration of the spot function over the subaperture pixels to compute the variance of phase estimates reconstructed from Shack-Hartmann slope measurements. The model of slope variances, which is simply Eq. (162) divided by $2(2\pi)^2$, agreed well with wave-optics simulations over a range of atmospheric conditions characterized by d/r_0 and Rytov number.

6.4   Hybrid WFS Architecture

Using two WFS's requires splitting of the available light, which must be done optimally to avoid excessive variance in the measurements that would negate any benefits of a hybrid approach. The choice of subaperture size for each WFS is the first step in determining the optimal splitting, since this controls the relative num-

143

ber of photons available for each sensor's measurements. The models described in Secs. 6.2 and 6.3 provide a useful means of determining optimum subaperture sizes. Normalizing the error models by $(d/r_0)^2$ aids the comparative analysis by enforcing the condition that each WFS works with a fixed number of photons within an area equal to the square of the atmospheric coherence area r_0^2. Figure 46 shows normalized phase variances from the models given by Eqs. (160) and (162) without scintillation for values of d/r_0 between 0.25 and 1. For each phase-variance model, r_0 was set to 7.5cm, the full-aperture size was set to $16.5 \times r_0$, and the SH WFS had two pixels per diffraction angle and eight pixels across each subaperture's detector array, and the phase variances from the models were then normalized by $(d/r_0)^2$. Figure 46 (a) shows the normalized models for 400 photons per subaperture and 10% SRI fiber-coupling efficiency, and Fig. 46 (b) shows the results for 800 photons per subaperture and 40% coupling efficiency. The case used for the plot in Fig. 46 (a) represents bad but realistic conditions for the SRI, while the case used for (b) uses a more optimistic value for coupling efficiency but still a quite low level of light [75]. These plots suggest that the SH WFS should provide the most benefit in a hybrid WFS when the SRI's coupling efficiency becomes very low. Also, as the input number of photons increases, the performance of both WFS's improve while maintaining the same performance relative to one another.

The minimum phase variance predicted by the models within the range $0 \leq d/r_0 \leq 1$ occurs when the SRI subapertures have side lengths $d_{\mathrm{sri}} \approx 0.5 \times r_0$ and when the SH subapertures are as large as possible. AO systems using SH WFS's can achieve closed-loop Strehl ratios of about 0.75 with as few as 500 photons per subaperture when $d/r_0 = 1$, but their performance degrades steadily as d/r_0 increases due to undersampling of the incident field [90]. Therefore, the hybrid WFS was designed to have $d_{\mathrm{sh}}/r_0 = 1$ and $d_{\mathrm{sri}}/r_0 = 1/2$. The plots in Fig. 46 also show that, especially in low-light conditions and low SRI-coupling efficiencies, the SH phase variance tends to be significantly lower than the SRI phase variance. Therefore, larger SH subapertures

144

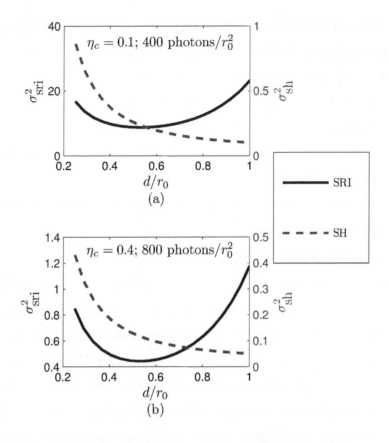

Figure 46:   SRI and SH phase variances from models

also require less light to be split from the SRI to achieve equal phase variances between the two WFS's.

Besides allowing for less light to be split from the SRI in a hybrid architecture, larger SH subapertures decrease the time required to read out the SH-spot irradiances from the detector array, which is typically the longest delay in the wavefront-estimation process [66]. When the SH subapertures are designed to have two pixels per diffraction-limited angle, eight pixels across the subaperture generally provide plenty of room to avoid significant truncation errors or crosstalk [41]. With eight pixels across SH subapertures that have twice the side length of the SRI subapertures (and therefore half the number of subapertures across the pupil), the same number of pixels must be read from both the SH and SRI sensors (recall that each SRI subaperture requires four pixels in the detector array), which can be done simultaneously. Therefore, the proposed architecture does not operate any slower than a comparable stand-alone SRI. This characteristic would be beneficial if, for example, the SH measurements required less frequent temporal sampling. Since the models make no assumptions about integration times, longer integration time in the SH would translate to less light being split from the SRI, which should improve the hybrid's performance even more. Therefore, future work in temporal analysis of the hybrid WFS could lead to additional performance gains.

Combining phase estimates from SRI measurements and SH measurements requires some discussion of the alignment between WFS subapertures and DM actuators, especially for a hybrid WFS that uses two sensors with different subaperture sizes. The SRI alignment geometry is conceptually simple; DM actuators are aligned with the centers of the SRI subapertures, which is where SRI field estimates are assumed to form subaperture-averages of the incident optical field [3, 6]. Shack-Hartmann alignment geometries are slightly more complicated, however, since the actuator locations must be aligned with the SH subapertures based on assumptions about the relationships between the phase of the incident field and the locations of the SH slope measurements. Different geometries can be used to relate SH slope measurements to locations of phase estimates (or actuators). The popular Fried geometry aligns the actuators with the corners of the SH subapertures [28]. The Southwell geometry locates the actuators at the centers of the SH subapertures, while the Hudgin geometry estimates the phase along the edges of the subapertures [40, 76].

The multiple geometries can be useful in forming better SH phase estimates at a denser grid of actuators than can be done simply by interpolating estimates from a single geometry. Since the Southwell geometry actually averages adjacent SH slope measurements and reconstructs phase estimates from these averaged slopes using a Hudgin geometry, it is a natural complement to the phase reconstructed using the Fried geometry. Figure 47 shows the Fried and Southwell geometries overlaid with

146

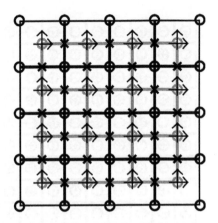

Figure 47:   SH slope-reconstruction geometries

Arrows show locations of slope measurements, ×'s show locations of averages of adjacent slope measurements. Black lines and circles show the SH subapertures and actuator locations for the Fried geometry. Gray lines and circles show the virtual subapertures and actuator locations for the Southwell geometry.

one another. The black arrows show the locations of SH slope measurements, and the black ×'s show the locations of the averages of adjacent slope measurements. Black grid lines and circles show the SH subapertures and actuator locations for the Fried geometry, and gray grid lines and circles show the virtual subapertures and actuator locations for the Southwell geometry.

Figure 48 shows the proposed hybrid architecture with two SRI-subaperture side lengths per SH-subaperture side length, where the center of every other SRI subaperture is aligned with the corner of a SH subaperture. The black lines show the outline of the SRI subapertures, the gray lines show the SH subapertures, the circles indicate the locations of SRI estimates (and DM actuators), the dots indicate the locations of SH estimates using the Fried geometry, and the plus signs show the locations of the SH estimates using the Southwell geometry. In this architecture, the hybrid WFS computes SH phase estimates by linearly interpolating phase estimates from both the Fried and Southwell geometries and then averages the resulting two

147

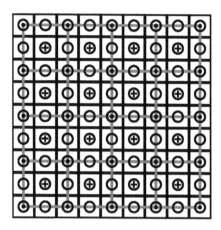

Figure 48:   Hybrid-WFS alignment geometry

Black lines show outline of SRI subapertures, gray lines show SH subapertures, circles show locations of SRI phase estimates, dots (·) show locations of SH phase estimates using the Fried reconstruction geometry, and plus signs (+) show locations of SH phase estimates using the Southwell reconstruction geometry.

grids of phase estimates. This average of SH phase estimates is then combined with the SRI phase estimates using a weighted-average approach as described in Sec. 6.5 below.

6.5   Maximum-Likelihood, Weighted-Average Hybrid WFS

A successful hybrid architecture that combines multiple WFS's should favor the WFS that is best-suited to provide phase estimates for the beacon and atmospheric conditions at hand and shift phase-estimating responsibility to the other WFS(s) as conditions change. A weighted-average, maximum-likelihood estimate (MLE) provides this type of control and is applicable to SH and SRI phase measurements with noise that is well-approximated as having a Gaussian probability density function (pdf). Although the phase-variance models of Secs. 6.2 and 6.3 were developed from the assumption of Poisson-distributed photocount noise, the operations used to produce LS-reconstructed/unwrapped phase estimates justify a Gaussian pdf based on the central-limit theorem. The central-limit theorem applies to LS-reconstructed/unwrapped phase estimates since they are essentially the average of phase estimates resulting from all possible integration paths over the computed phase differences [29].

Given two noisy measurements ϕ_1 and ϕ_2 with equal means ϕ_0, but different variances σ_1^2 and σ_2^2 due to noise from two different sensors, the maximum-likelihood estimate for normally distributed noise is a weighted average. To determine the weighting that provides the MLE, the noise is assumed independent between phase measurements and the joint pdf is formed as the product of the two Gaussian pdf's given by

$$p_\Phi(\phi_1) = \frac{1}{\sigma_1\sqrt{2\pi}} \exp\left[-\frac{(\phi_1 - \phi_0)^2}{2\sigma_1^2}\right]$$
$$p_\Phi(\phi_2) = \frac{1}{\sigma_2\sqrt{2\pi}} \exp\left[-\frac{(\phi_2 - \phi_0)^2}{2\sigma_2^2}\right]. \tag{169}$$

The joint probability of observing ϕ_1 and ϕ_2 given an input ϕ_0 is then given by

$$\begin{aligned} f(\phi_1, \phi_2|\phi_0) &= p_\Phi(\phi_1)p_\Phi(\phi_2) \\ &= \frac{1}{2\pi\sigma_1\sigma_2} \exp\left\{-\left[\frac{(\phi_1 - \phi_0)^2}{2\sigma_1^2} + \frac{(\phi_2 - \phi_0)^2}{2\sigma_2^2}\right]\right\}. \end{aligned} \tag{170}$$

This joint pdf provides an expression for the likelihood that the input is actually equal to ϕ_0 given observed measurements of ϕ_1 and ϕ_2, which leads to the log-likelihood function given by

$$\ell(\phi_0|\phi_1, \phi_2) = \ln\left[f(\phi_1, \phi_2|\phi_0)\right]. \tag{171}$$

Setting $d\ell(\phi_0|\phi_1, \phi_2)/d\phi_0 = 0$ and solving for ϕ_0 leads to the MLE for ϕ_0 given noisy measurements ϕ_1 and ϕ_2

$$\hat{\phi} = \frac{\sigma_2^2}{\sigma_1^2 + \sigma_2^2}\phi_1 + \frac{\sigma_1^2}{\sigma_1^2 + \sigma_2^2}\phi_2. \tag{172}$$

This analysis started from the assumption that the phase measurements of each WFS were unbiased. If, however, either or both of the WFS's had some measurable scaling or bias in the phase estimates, the preceding analysis could be easily adapted to account for it by including scaling and bias terms that operate on the mean phase ϕ_0 in the log-likelihood function. The resulting weights would then include the scaling and bias terms, and the estimate would still be unbiased as long as the scaling and bias were accurately characterized. However, for this study, the SH and SRI phase estimates are assumed to be unbiased, which should generally be true for well-designed sensors. The salient point here is that the weighted-average, maximum-likelihood hybrid phase estimate given by Eq. (172) is unbiased, even if the individual-WFS measurements are not. Because the hybrid phase estimate is an unbiased estimator, the Cramer-Rao lower bound (CRLB) on its variance is given by [7]

$$
\begin{aligned}
\mathrm{Var}\left(\hat{\phi} - \phi_0\right) &\geq \frac{1}{\left\langle \left[\frac{\partial}{\partial \phi_0}\ell(\phi_0|\phi_1, \phi_2)\right]^2 \right\rangle} \\
&= \left(\frac{1}{\sigma_1^2} + \frac{1}{\sigma_2^2}\right)^{-1}.
\end{aligned}
\tag{173}
$$

Applying the results of the preceding analysis to phase measurements from the SRI and SH WFS's, a hybrid WFS can be formed as the weighted average of the SRI phase esimate $\hat{\phi}_{\mathrm{sri}}$ and the SH phase estimate $\hat{\phi}_{\mathrm{sh}}$ as

$$
\hat{\phi} = a\hat{\phi}_{\mathrm{sri}} + b\hat{\phi}_{\mathrm{sh}},
\tag{174}
$$

where a and b are the weights of the phase estimates from the SRI and SH WFS's, respectively. The phase-error variance $\sigma_{\hat{\phi}}^2$ of the hybrid WFS's phase estimate is given by

$$
\begin{aligned}
\sigma_{\hat{\phi}}^2 &= a^2\sigma_{\mathrm{sri}}^2 + b^2\sigma_{\mathrm{sh}}^2 \\
&= \left(\frac{\sigma_{\mathrm{sh}}^2}{\sigma_{\mathrm{sri}}^2 + \sigma_{\mathrm{sh}}^2}\right)^2 \sigma_{\mathrm{sri}}^2 + \left(\frac{\sigma_{\mathrm{sri}}^2}{\sigma_{\mathrm{sri}}^2 + \sigma_{\mathrm{sh}}^2}\right)^2 \sigma_{\mathrm{sh}}^2,
\end{aligned}
\tag{175}
$$

where the weights a and b have been defined using Eq. (172) with $\sigma_1^2 = \sigma_{\text{sri}}^2$ and $\sigma_2^2 = \sigma_{\text{sh}}^2$. With a little algebraic manipulation, Eq. (175) reduces exactly to Eq. (173). Therefore, the hybrid WFS's phase variance achieves the CRLB. Note that for two component WFS's with equal variances, the variance of the hybrid WFS's estimate is half that of either stand-alone WFS's. Also, for complementary WFS's, it is conceivable that conditions that degrade one WFS's performance will improve the performance of the other WFS. When the hybrid WFS is composed of two complementary WFS's, the variance of its measurements should be very stable.

Substituting the models from Eqs. (160) and (162) into Eq. (175) provides a model that facilitates optimal design of the weighted-average hybrid WFS. Because a and b are defined such that $a + b = 1$, both weights for the maximum-likelihood estimate can be quickly computed from only one of the weights, say a, which is a function of the ratio of the phase-variance models given by Eqs. (160) and (162). The resulting expression is simplified somewhat by first defining the number of photons available to the SRI and SH WFS's in terms of the number of input photons K_{in}, a splitting parameter γ that is defined as the fraction of input optical power sent to the SRI, and the ratio of SH-subaperture side length to SRI-subaperture side length $r_d = d_{\text{sh}}/d_{\text{sri}}$. The number of photons sent to the SRI and SH WFS's can then be related to the input photons by

$$
\begin{aligned}
K_{\text{sri}} &= \gamma K_{\text{in}} \left(\frac{d}{r_0}\right)^2 \\
K_{\text{sh}} &= r_d^2 (1 - \gamma) K_{\text{in}} \left(\frac{d}{r_0}\right)^2,
\end{aligned}
\tag{176}
$$

where d is the actuator spacing of the deformable mirror used to apply the wavefront correction, which is equal to the side length of the SRI subaperture d_{sri}. The ratio r_d allows investigation of the impact of SH subapertures that are potentially larger than the SRI subapertures, which could result in more efficient use of the input light. The number of input photons K_{in} is defined as the number of photons in an area with side length r_0 incident on the receive aperture of the hybrid WFS. Therefore, assuming

151

$\beta = 1/2$ and expressing the amount of power in the reference leg of the hybrid's SRI in terms of the coupling efficiency, the phase variances of the hybrid's SRI and SH WFS's can be expressed as

$$\sigma_{\text{sri}}^2 = \frac{2}{\gamma(d/r_0)^2 K_{\text{in}}\sqrt{\eta_c}\,\mathcal{V}}(\tilde{\sigma}_I^2 + 1)^{3/4} \tag{177}$$

$$\sigma_{\text{sh}}^2 = 2\frac{(2\pi)^2}{r_d^2(1-\gamma)(d/r_0)^2 K_{\text{in}}}\mathcal{U}(\tilde{\sigma}_I^2 + 1). \tag{178}$$

where $\mathcal{U} \triangleq \sum_{i=1}^{N^2} x_i^2 f_i$. It is important to recognize that the numerical integrations used to compute the SH phase variance are performed over the area defined by the SH subaperture side length d_{sh}. Therefore, although actuator spacing d (or equivalently SRI subaperture size d_{sri}) is used to compute K_{sh}, the numerical integrations to determine σ_{sh}^2 from Eq. (162) must be done over an area defined by $(d \cdot r_d)^2$. Also, for the computation of the normalized angular SH subaperture-pixel coordinate x_i in Eq. (162), the diffraction angle is defined by $\lambda/d_{\text{sh}} = \lambda/(d \cdot r_d)$. The weighting on the SRI phase estimate that results in a maximum-likelihood estimate can then be expressed as

$$
\begin{aligned}
a &= \frac{\sigma_{\text{sh}}^2}{\sigma_{\text{sri}}^2 + \sigma_{\text{sh}}^2} \\
&= \left(1 + \frac{\sigma_{\text{sri}}^2}{\sigma_{\text{sh}}^2}\right)^{-1} \\
&= \left[1 + r_d^2\left(\frac{1-\gamma}{\gamma}\right)\left(\frac{1+\eta_c}{\eta_c}\right)\frac{(\tilde{\sigma}_I^2 + 1)^{-1/4}}{\mathcal{V}\mathcal{U}}\right]^{-1}.
\end{aligned} \tag{179}
$$

Figure 49 shows a surface plot of the SRI weighting as a function of scintillation index and coupling efficiency for 3200 photons/r_0^2, $\gamma = 0.5$, and $r_d = 2$. This plot shows the MLE weighting favors the SRI as the strength of scintillation increases, which is desirable since previous studies have shown that the SRI is less sensitive to scintillation than the Shack-Hartmann [3]. The plot also shows that the MLE weighting is a much stronger function of coupling efficiency, and as the SRI's coupling

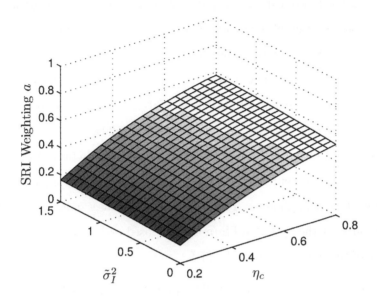

Figure 49:   Weighting of SRI estimate
Computed for 50% of the power sent to each when 3200 photons/r_0^2 were split between both WFS's.

efficiency decreases, the MLE more strongly favors the Shack-Hartmann WFS, which is completely independent of the SRI's coupling efficiency. In closed-loop operation, this action should help to maximize the SRI's coupling efficiency since a decrease in residual phase variance should result in higher Strehl ratios and therefore greater coupling efficiency.

The expression for the hybrid's phase variance given by Eq. (175) reduces to the expression for the CRLB in Eq. (173). Therefore, the hybrid phase estimate is efficient because it achieves equality in the CRLB, which means that it results in a minimum-variance estimate for WFS measurements with given variances. However, the models from Secs. 6.2 and 6.3 show that the variances of the individual WFS's in the hybrid are a function of critical design parameters. The phase variance given by Eq. (175), which can be evaluated numerically, helps choose optimal design parameters. This approach was used to determine the optimal architecture discussed in Sec. 6.4. The models of phase variance can also help determine the value of the splitting parameter γ. Figure 50 shows a plot of the hybrid phase variance versus γ for coupling efficiencies of 20%, 40%, and 80%. These values represent a range of coupling efficiencies from optimistic to ideal [61, 75]. The maximum achievable coupling efficiency for an ideal point source in perfect seeing conditions is $\approx$80%, but coupling efficiency decreases rapidly with increasing D/r_0, becoming greater than 20% only when $D/r_0 > 4$ and rapid image stabilization is used [75]. The model for the hybrid WFS's phase-error variance shows that as coupling efficiency decreases, more light should be split to the SRI to offset the loss of photons. This suggests that in cases of low coupling efficiency, the best results for the hybrid WFS in the proposed architecture should be achieved when most of the light is split to the SRI.

For the plots in Fig. 50, the weighting on the SRI estimate was set to $a = 1/2$, the input number of photons per r_0^2 was set to 3200, and the SH-subaperture side length was twice that of the SRI, which was selected to control two actuators/r_0, $i.e.$ $d/r_0 = d_{\mathrm{sri}}/r_0 = 1/2$. The black $\times$-markers identify the locations of the minimum phase variance. Substituting the values of γ that resulted in minimum phase variances along with the other applicable design parameters into Eq. (179) then provides the weighting required to perform the MLE.

The superior performance of the SRI in strong scintillation comes from the fact that it directly produces principal-value phase measurements. However, unwrapping SRI phase measurements still requires least-squares reconstruction of phase differences. In strong scintillation, the non-least-squares component contributes significantly to the atmospheric phase [29]. The SRI's ability to measure the non-least-squares phase explains its superior performance relative to the SH WFS in strong scintillation. However, because the SH WFS has been shown to outperform the SRI in weak scintillation, it may be that the SH is better than the SRI at estimating the least-squares phase. Combining the two WFS's into a hybrid in the maximum-likelihood, weighted-average approach described here provides a means of shifting wavefront-sensing responsibilities to the WFS best suited for whatever scintillation

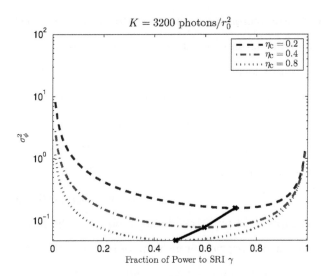

Figure 50:   Choosing optimum splitting parameter γ

conditions are encountered by the AO system. The following section provides results of wave-optics tests comparing the least-squares phase-estimating performance of the maximum-likelihood, weighted-average hybrid WFS with that of a stand-alone SRI.

6.6   *Wave-Optics Tests of Hybrid-WFS Performance*

Wave-optics simulations provide a means of evaluating sensor performance on atmospherically propagated fields, especially when beacons are scintillated by propagation through volume-distributed atmospheric turbulence [3–5]. Therefore, to test hybrid-WFS performance, numerically generated optical fields served as inputs to the hybrid's SRI and SH WFS's as well as a stand-alone SRI WFS, which served as a basis for comparison to the hybrid's performance. The primary performance metric employed was the phase-estimation Strehl ratio (PES), which measures how well a WFS estimates the phase of an incident optical field. The PES is computed from the field-estimation Strehl ratio defined as [64]

$$S\left[U(\boldsymbol{r}'), \hat{U}(\boldsymbol{r}')\right] = \frac{\left\langle \left|\sum_{i=1}^{N_a^2} U(\boldsymbol{r}')\hat{U}^*(\boldsymbol{r}')\right|^2 \right\rangle}{\left\langle \sum_{i=1}^{N_a^2} U(\boldsymbol{r}')U^*(\boldsymbol{r}')\right\rangle \left\langle \sum_{i=1}^{N_a^2} \hat{U}(\boldsymbol{r}')\hat{U}^*(\boldsymbol{r}')\right\rangle}, \qquad (180)$$

155

where $\boldsymbol{r}'$ is a coordinate vector indicating actuator locations, $U(\boldsymbol{r}')$ contains the complex-field values at the actuator locations, $\hat{U}(\boldsymbol{r}')$ contains the estimated complex-field values at the actuator locations, N_a is the number of actuators across the DM, the asterisk indicates complex conjugation, and angle brackets indicate ensemble averages of the aperture-averaged values resulting from the summations. The PES is computed by evaluating $S\{U(\boldsymbol{r}'), \exp[j\hat{\phi}(\boldsymbol{r}')]\}$, where $\hat{\phi}(\boldsymbol{r}')$ contains the phase estimates at the actuator locations. The PES was evaluated for the LS phase estimates $\hat{\phi}_{\text{LS}}$ at the actuators as well as the LSPV-phase estimates $\hat{\phi}_{\text{LSPV}}$ linearly interpolated up to the size of the input grid with coordinate vector $\boldsymbol{r}$. The latter case evaluates $S\{U(\boldsymbol{r}), \exp[j\hat{\phi}_{\text{DM}}(\boldsymbol{r})]\}$, which provides a measure of how well the DM can correct the input optical field based on the phase estimates output by the WFS, $i.e.$ without amplitude correction. For this reason, the PES from interpolated LSPV-phase estimates $\hat{\phi}_{\text{DM}}$ is referred to as the DM phase-fitting Strehl ratio (DMPFS).

6.6.1 Atmospheric Fields. To test hybrid-WFS performance, optical fields were generated by numerically propagating an on-axis point source through 40 atmospheric realizations, each modeled by ten Kolmogorov phase screens. The phase screens were evenly spaced throughout the propagation path and designed to provide a total-path, spherical-wave atmospheric coherence width of $r_0 = 7.5$cm. Since the same simulated optical fields were used here as for the centroid-error study, further details on the wave-optics simulations can be found in Sec. 4.3.

6.6.2 Simulation Results. Several different approaches to determining the splitting parameter γ and weighting parameter a in the phase estimates for the hybrid WFS were simulated using the architecture discussed in Sec. 6.4. For the first case, the light was evenly split between the hybrid's SH and SRI sensors, and the phase estimates from each were evenly weighted. For the second case, the phase estimates were evenly weighted, but the splitting was determined with an optimizing procedure that found the value for γ that minimized Eq. (175). For the third case, the light was evenly split between sensors, but the weighting was determined using the MLE for

156

the SRI weighting given by Eq. (179). In the fourth case, an initial value of 0.5 was used for γ to determine the MLE weighting, which was then used in Eq. (175) to find the optimum γ, after which the MLE weights were determined using this optimum value for γ in Eq. (179).

Figure 51 (a) shows the LS-phase-estimation Strehl ratio (LSPES) for these four cases along with the LSPES for a comparable stand-alone SRI WFS. The hybrid WFS split the same number of photons received by the stand-alone SRI between its SH and SRI sensors. The simulations used a value of 10% for fiber-coupling efficiency and a value of 200 for the number of photons per r_0^2. The variances of the LSPES are also shown in Fig. 51 (b). These plots show that the hybrid WFS performs better than a comparable stand-alone SRI at estimating the LS phase for this case of low coupling efficiency and low number of photons in all four cases of splitting and weighting. Also, the results show that the splitting optimization and MLE weighting do improve hybrid performance compared to arbitrarily setting the values of the splitting and weighting. The performance gains of the hybrid are essentially the same throughout the range of Rytov numbers used as is evident from Fig 52, which shows the LSPES performance of the four hybrid approaches relative to the stand-alone SRI.

Figure 51 (b) shows that variability in the hybrid's performance tends to be much lower than that of the SRI, especially at Rytov numbers where the hybrid has higher mean LSPES. The lower variance suggests greater stability in the hybrid, which maintains higher levels of performance in atmospheric conditions that cause the stand-alone SRI's performance to drop significantly. This is further illustrated in Fig. 53, which shows the LSPES for every realization in the case of no scintillation (propagation distance $L = 0$km). The greater stability and decreased Strehl-ratio variance is a key advantage of the hybrid WFS, since stability and Strehl-ratio variance have been identified as challenges for the SRI [42]. Results in Fig. 53 (a) are for the case of 10% coupling efficiency and 200 photons per r_0^2, and Fig. 53 (b) shows results for the case of 40% coupling efficiency and 3200 photons/r_0^2. At the higher

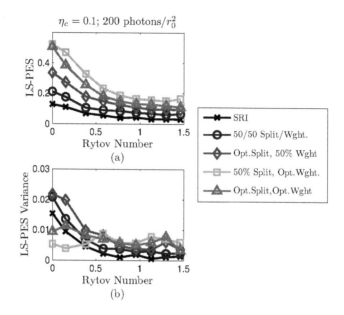

Figure 51: Hybrid wave-optics LSPES Vs. Rytov number
LS-phase-estimation Strehl ratio for four approaches to optimizing the hybrid WFS
compared with a stand-alone SRI.

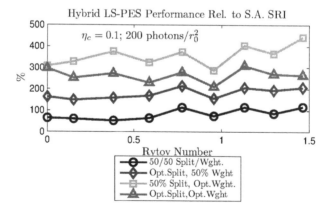

Figure 52: Hybrid's LSPES improvement over SRI
LSPES Improvement of Hybrid WFS relative to stand-alone SRI for four approaches
to optimizing.

coupling efficiency and higher light level, the stand-alone SRI does quite well, but its performance still occasionally drops significantly below that of the hybrid.

Figure 54 more clearly shows the improvement of the hybrid WFS's LSPES compared with comparable stand-alone SRI and SH WFS's. The plot in Fig. 54 (a) shows the LSPES for all three WFS's, and the plot in (b) shows the percent improvement of the hybrid's LSPES over both stand-alone WFS's. The hybrid WFS's performance improvement over the stand-alone WFS's is a result of the decrease in phase variance inherent in the MLE approach discussed in Sec. 6.5. It is interesting that the hybrid's improvement over the stand-alone SRI does not significantly depend on scintillation strength, whereas the hybrid WFS shows less improvement over the stand-alone SH WFS in weaker scintillation with its improvement increasing as scintillation strength increases. This is consistent with the fact that the SH WFS's phase error increases significantly with increasing scintillation strength, while the SRI is less sensitive to scintillation strength. Also, the poor performance shown by the SRI in Fig. 54 is a result of the low coupling efficiency used, which decreases fringe visibility and increases the variance of the SRI's phase estimates. For higher fiber-coupling efficiency, $e.g.$ $\eta_c = 40\%$, the stand-alone SRI does much better than the $\eta_c = 10\%$ case shown in Fig. 54 and outperforms the stand-alone SH WFS across the whole range of scintillation strengths. However, even at 40% coupling efficiency, the hybrid WFS still outperforms the stand-alone SRI. Also, for all values of coupling efficiency examined, the simulation data shows the SRI's sensitivity to scintillation when photon noise is included, which is consistent with experimental results reported by Corley and Rhoadarmer in [18]. The data in Fig. 54 resulted from applying 50/50 splitting with optimal weighting and was generated by simulations independent from those that generated the results shown in Figs. 51 and 52.

It is important to emphasize that for these simulations, the atmospheric conditions at each realization were independent of all other realizations. Therefore, the hybrid's ability to maintain high levels of performance when the SRI's performance degrades illustrates a significant potential advantage of the hybrid in closed-loop op-

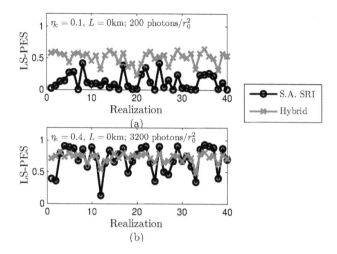

Figure 53:   Stability of hybrid's LSPES

LSPES for all realizations of the optimum splitting, optimum weighting approach to the hybrid WFS in the absence of scintillation.

eration. In realistic operating conditions, it is reasonable to expect a given set of atmospheric conditions to be present for many iterations of the AO control loop. Also, in closed-loop AO systems, bad compensation lingers in the DM commands due to the integral control law [53]. Therefore, steadier open-loop performance suggests steadier closed-loop performance because the hybrid WFS would be able to maintain higher Strehl ratios even when the SRI's performance drops. Furthermore, in closed-loop operation, the hybrid WFS could collect real-time measurements such as the SRI's coupling efficiency and a running average of the residual phase variance of the SH and SRI phase estimates to determine the optimum splitting parameter and MLE weighting. Therefore, in closed-loop operation, the worst that the hybrid WFS could do would be to match the performance of a comparable SRI.

The SRI has the unique ability to estimate the principal-value phase, which is necessary for decreasing unwrapping errors in the presence of branch points [60]. Even though the hybrid has been shown to outperform a stand-alone SRI at estimating the LS phase, a natural question arises as to whether it can perform as well at producing

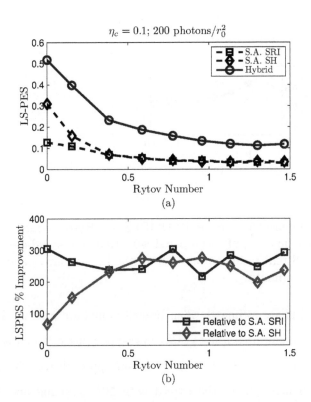

Figure 54: Hybrid's performance compared to SRI & SH WFS's
LSPES for the SRI & SH WFS's compared with that from the hybrid (a) and the
percent improvement shown by the hybrid over both stand-alone WFS's.

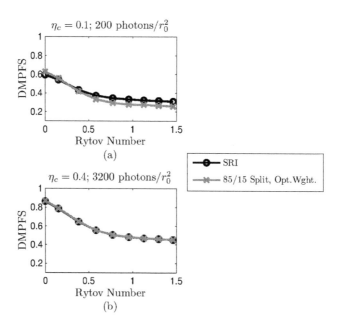

Figure 55:   Hybrid's DMPFS Vs. Rytov number

Performance of the hybrid WFS compared with that of a stand-alone SRI using the DM phase-fitting Strehl ratio computed from the least-squares- and principal-value-unwrapped-phase estimates.

LSPV-unwrapped phase estimates when branch points are present. Figure 55 shows the DMPFS metric computed using LSPV-unwrapped phase estimates compared with a comparable stand-alone SRI. The optimization approach was slightly different for the results shown here. Since the hybrid with 50% splitting and MLE weighting performed best in the earlier studies, as shown in Fig. 51, a similar approach was chosen for the LSPV-phase-estimation performance study, except 85% of the light was sent to the hybrid's SRI. This provided enough light to the SH for improving the hybrid's LS-phase estimates while at the same time ensuring plenty of light was available to the SRI for estimation of the principal-value phase. Evaluation of the individual realizations, however, shows the promise of improved hybrid performance in closed-loop operation.

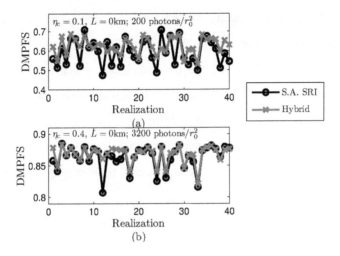

Figure 56:   Ensembles of hybrid's DMPFS

Illustration of the stability of the hybrid's performance at matching the phase of the input field using least-squares and principal-value phase estimates when SRI performance drops.

Figure 56 (a) shows the DMPFS for all realizations in the case of 10% coupling efficiency and low light, while Fig. 56 (b) shows the results for 40% coupling efficiency and a higher light level. Both cases continue to show that the hybrid performance remains high during realizations when the SRI's performance dips significantly. Again, this behavior promises increased stability for the hybrid WFS in closed-loop operation.

6.7   Conclusion

This work has developed a hybrid WFS that combines SH-WFS measurements with SRI measurements in a robust, flexible architecture that shows performance gains over a stand-alone SRI in open-loop wave-optics simulations for a range of atmospheric conditions. The weighted-average MLE ensures the hybrid's phase-estimation algorithm favors the WFS most suited to the atmoshperic and beacon conditions at hand. When the proposed architecture is placed in a closed-loop AO system, the result should be much more stable operation and will also offer additional performance gains through real-time adjustments to the splitting parameter and weighting coefficients based on measurements of SRI coupling efficiency and the variance of the sensor measurements. The hybrid WFS performs especially well compared to a stand-alone SRI in cases of low SRI coupling efficiency, which promises an improved ability to close the AO control loop. Adding correlation-based capabilities to enable phase estimation with extended beacons will further enhance the hybrid's performance and provide better AO compensation with uncooperative targets while avoiding complicated solutions like a bootstrap beacon, Zernike tomography, or gradient-descent tomography.

VII. Conclusion

This work has shown, for the first time, that a hybrid WFS formed by combining a SH WFS and an SRI performs better in open-loop simulation than a comparable stand-alone WFS. The improved performance was indicated by higher estimation Strehl ratio for the least-squares phase than computed for a comparable SRI. Also, the variance of estimation Strehl ratio was lower in the hybrid than for a stand-alone SRI in both least-squares- and LSPV-reconstructed phase estimates. Further, on average the hybrid matched a stand-alone SRI's LSPV-reconstructed-phase-estimation Strehl ratio and had much higher Strehl ratios in atmospheric realizations that caused significant degradation in the stand-alone SRI. The hybrid design was based on detailed analysis that provided new models for the impact of photon noise coupled with scintillation on phase-estimation errors for the SH WFS and the SRI. These noise models aided in critical design choices and enabled the formation of a weighted-average, maximum-likelihood phase-estimation algorithm for the hybrid. Also, for the first time, a noise model for the SRI predicts its sensitivity to scintillation strength, which has been observed in laboratory experiments but not previously predicted by theory [63].

7.1 Model of SH-WFS Centroid Error

Chapter IV presents a model for centroid error due to shot noise and scintillation. When scintillation is absent, the model reduces to the standard model assumed for photon noise only. Also, for subaperture sizes smaller than the atmospheric coherence width, the model can be adjusted to account for aberrations caused by the atmosphere. The model matches results of wave-optics simulations reasonably well. If enough light is available, the centroid-error variance due to scintillation and photon noise becomes relatively insensitive to scintillation. However, at low light levels, it is significantly impacted by scintillation in the weak regime. Also, at low light levels in small subapertures relative to r_0, the centroid-error variance becomes a significant part of the overall centroid variance.

The model is presented in a general form for any shape of intensity distribution and can be evaluated by numerically integrating over a complicated shape function or by assuming a simple shape function to attain more analytical solutions. Previously developed models that assumed constant intensity can be adjusted to account for scintillation using the model presented here. Finally, the presented model of centroid-error variance could be developed further by recognizing it as a conditional centroid variance and applying the conditional centroid variance formula to examine the impact of factors such as random centroid displacement and spot size.

7.2 Model of SRI Phase Error

Chapter V provides an analytical model for the shot-noise-induced error variance of phase estimates computed from SRI measurements. The model was tested against both Monte Carlo and wave-optics simulations and was shown to agree reasonably well over a fairly wide range of atmospheric conditions. The model also predicted the dependence of SRI estimation error on scintillation, which has been observed in laboratory experiments.

7.3 Hybrid WFS

Chapter VI presents a hybrid WFS that combines SH-WFS measurements with SRI measurements in a robust, flexible architecture that shows performance gains over a stand-alone SRI in open-loop wave-optics simulations for a range of atmospheric conditions. The noise models developed in Chapters IV and V enabled maximum-likelihood analysis, which lead to a weighted-averaging approach to the hybrid WFS that exploits the strengths and mitigates the weaknesses of each component WFS. The hybrid WFS performed especially well compared to a stand-alone SRI in cases of low SRI coupling efficiency, which promises an improved ability to close the AO control loop.

7.4 *Research Challenges*

A number of challenges were encountered and overcome during this research. First, the choice of alignment geometry in the hybrid's architecture was not a trivial matter. The SH and SRI WFS's could be aligned, and phase estimates could be formed from their measurements in a number of different ways. For example, the initial hybrid-WFS architecture explored in this work did not reconstruct the SH slopes into phase estimates, but instead combined the slope measurements with SRI piston measurements to approximate the wavefront by tiled planes [22]. While this approach was partially successful, the noise analysis for each WFS showed its limitations and lead to the pursuit of other alignment geometries and estimation algorithms, which ultimately lead to the approach presented in Ch. VI.

The noise models also turned out to be quite challenging. A great deal of effort was involved in getting the models to match Monte Carlo and wave-optics simulation results. This verification was essential to ensuring that the models were accurate, especially since both models involved some amount of numerical computations. At one point, the verification with simulation became something of an impediment as issues related to undersampling caused simulation results that did not agree with the model for the SH's centroid error. However, the effort ultimately lead to much better SH simulations as well as validation of the noise model. This issue motivated the approach of first verifying the noise models with Monte Carlo simulations before moving on to wave-optics simulations. The Monte Carlo and wave-optics simulations for the SH noise study turned out to be so similar that only the wave-optics results were presented in Ch. IV. However, the SRI wave-optics and Monte Carlo results did not match each other and the noise model quite as well. In fact, the results of the Monte Carlo simulations were used to reveal initial problems and subsequently correct them, which ultimately lead to a better agreement between wave-optics results and the noise model.

Another issue that complicated the noise analysis is the fact that scintillation remains poorly understood. Intensity statistics for scintillated optical fields have generally been developed based on heuristic arguments that conceptualize scintillation effects as resulting from modulation and filtering processes [1, 71]. In fact, wave-optics simulations have shown better agreement with experiment than theoretical predictions [1, 25]. Therefore, it is difficult to evaluate the fidelity of wave-optics results without anchoring them to experiments. However, as mentioned in Ch. I, computer simulations, in contrast to hardware experiments, provided flexibility in design choices for hybrid architectures and enabled robust testing of the hybrid WFS's phase-estimation algorithms. Also, wave-optics simulations enabled investigation of centroid error in conditions that could not be reproduced experimentally, for example when photon levels are too low to guarantee shot-noise limited performance of commercially available sensors.

7.5   Future Work

The proposed hybrid WFS should be tested in wave-optics simulations of closed-loop AO performance. When the proposed hybrid architecture is placed in a closed-loop AO system, the result should be much more stable operation and should also offer performance gains through real-time adjustments to the splitting parameter and weighting coefficients based on measurements of SRI coupling efficiency and the variance of the sensor measurements. Closed-loop simulations will test this assertion and may identify other challenges or potential benefits related to implementing a hybrid WFS. If closed-loop simulations show promise for the hybrid WFS, the next step would be building and testing a hybrid WFS prototype.

Exploiting the SH WFS's capabilities to enable phase estimation with extended beacons should be explored to determine whether the hybrid WFS might also be able to perform adequately with extended beacons. This will require selection of a suitable algorithm for wavefront sensing with extended beacons based on analysis of the performance of extended-beacon approaches over a range of scintillation strengths and light levels. If possible, noise models similar to the one developed for centroid error in Ch. IV would be helpful in this analysis. Also, the impact of extended beacons on SRI performance needs to be better characterized to determine the range of beacon sizes for which it might suffer as well as to determine whether the SRI may perform acceptably with some cases of extended beacons.

A great deal of work could be done to evaluate different alignment geometries and algorithms for the hybrid WFS. Time constraints did not allow investigation of potential performance improvements related to the density of the SH subapertures. Perhaps more SH subapertures with fewer pixels per subaperture would lead to better hybrid performance than was shown here. Also, a modal approach to reconstruction of SH slopes into phase may be preferred to the zonal approach employed in this work and should be investigated. Additionally, the hybrid-WFS concept may eventually provide the best performance if it is merged with multiple-DM AO. For example, a multiple-DM, multiple-WFS approach may be better than multiple WFS's with a single DM or multiple DM's with a single WFS.

Ultimately, performing AO in deep turbulence is a difficult problem, and it seems likely that it will require a combination of approaches. Investigation of a hybrid WFS is one step towards combining proven AO technologies in a new way to seek performance improvements over a wider range of scintillation strengths, light levels, and beacon characteristics. The complementary natures of the SH and SRI WFS's show promise in a hybrid approach. This work has hopefully blazed a trail for future research to significantly advance AO technology by incorporating a SH/SRI hybrid WFS.

Bibliography

1. Andrews, Larry C. and Ronald L. Phillips. *Laser Beam Propagation through Random Media*. SPIE Press, Bellingham, WA, second edition, 2005.

2. Arrasmith, William W., Michael Roggemann, and Byron Welsh. "Optimal wavefront reconstruction for a coherent diffracted field". *Appl. Opt.*, 37(20):4457–4467, July 1998.

3. Barchers, D., Jeffrey, David L. Fried, Donald J. Link, Glenn A. Tyler, William Moretti, Terry J. Brennan, and Robert Q. Fugate. "The performance of wavefront sensors in strong scintillation". L. Wizinowich, Peter and Domenico Bonaccini (editors), *Adaptive Optical System Technologies II*, volume 4839. 2003.

4. Barchers, Jeffrey D., David L. Fried, and Donald J. Link. "Evaluation of the performance of a shearing interferometer in strong scintillation in the absence of additive measurement noise". *Appl. Opt.*, 41(18):3674–3683, June 2002.

5. Barchers, Jeffrey D., David L. Fried, and Donald J. Link. "Evaluation of the performance of Hartmann sensors in strong scintillation". *Appl. Opt.*, 41(6):1012–1021, February 2002.

6. Barchers, Jeffrey D. and Troy A. Rhoadarmer. "Evaluation of phase-shifting approaches for a point-diffraction interferometer with the mutual coherence function". *Appl. Opt.*, 41(36):7499–7509, December 2002.

7. Barrett, H., Harrison and Kyle J. Myers. *Foundations of Image Science*. John Wiley & Sons, Inc., 2004.

8. Barrett, Harrison H., Christopher Dainty, and David Lara. "Maximum-likelihood methods in wavefront sensing: stochastic models and likelihood functions". *J. Opt. Soc. Am. A*, 24(2):391–414, 2007. URL http://josaa.osa.org/abstract.cfm?URI=josaa-24-2-391.

9. Beland, Robert R. "Propagation through Atmospheric Optical Turbulence". Frederick G. Smith (editor), *Atmospheric Propagation of Radiation*, volume 2 of *The Infrared & Electro-Optical Systems Handbook*, chapter 2. Infrared Information Analysis Center and SPIE Opt. Eng. Press, 1993.

10. Belen'kii, Mikhail S., Jeff Barchers, Eric Berg, Don Bruns, Deborah Fung, Richard Gallant, Clay Kirk, Hope Runyeon, Vincent Rye, and Josh Voass. "Laboratory demonstration of wavefront based stochastic parallel gradient descent adaptive optics system". S.M. Hammel, A.M.J. van Eijk, M.T. Valley, and M.A. Vorontsov (editors), *Atmospheric Optics: Models, Measurements, and Target-in-the-Loop Propagation*, volume 6708. SPIE Proceedings, 2007.

11. Belen'kii, Mikhail S., Kevin Hughes, Hope Runyeon, and Vincent Rye. "Wavefront-based Stochastic Parallel Gradient Descent Beam Control". Troy

A. Rhoadarmer Richard A. Carreras, John D. Gonglewski (editor), *Advanced Wavefront Control: Methods, Devices, and Applications V*, volume 6711. SPIE Proceedings, 2007.

12. Belen'kii, Mikhail S., Vincent Rye, and Hope Runyeon. "Numerical Analysis of Hybrid Adaptive Optics System for Correcting Beacon Anisoplanatism and Thermal Blooming". Troy A. Rhoadarmer Richard A. Carreras, John D. Gonglewski (editor), *Advanced Wavefront Control: Methods, Devices, and Applications V*, volume 6711. SPIE Proceedings, 2007.

13. Boas, Mary L. *Mathematical Methods in the Physical Sciences*. John Wiley & Sons, third edition, 2006.

14. Born, Max and Emil Wolf. *Principles of Optics*. Cambridge University Press, New York, seventh (expanded) edition, 1999.

15. B.R.Hunt. "Matrix formulation of the reconstruction of phase values from phase differences". *J. Opt. Soc. Am.*, 69(3):393–399, March 1979.

16. Brigham, Oran. *Introduction to the Fourier Transform*. unk, New York, NY, first edition, 1998.

17. Cain, Stephen. "Design of an image projection correlating wavefront sensor for adaptive optics". *Opt. Eng.*, 43(7):1670–1681, 2004. URL `http://link.aip.org/link/?JOE/43/1670/1`.

18. Corley, Melissa S. and Troy A. Rhoadarmer. "Evaluation of phase-shifting techniques for a self-referencing interferometer wavefront sensor". volume 5894. SPIE, 2005. URL `http://link.aip.org/link/?PSI/5894/58940R/1`.

19. Coy, Steve. "Choosing mesh spacings and mesh dimensions for wave optics simulation". Mark T. Gruneisen, John D. Gonglewski, and Michael K. Giles (editors), *Advanced Wavefront Control: Methods, Devices, and Applications III*, volume 5894. 2005.

20. Crummett, William P. and Arthur B. Western. *University Physics: Models and Applications*. Wm. C. Brown Publishers, 1994.

21. van Dam, Marcos A. and Richard G. Lane. "Wave-front slope estimation". *J. Opt. Soc. Am. A*, 17(7):1319–1324, 2000. URL `http://josaa.osa.org/abstract.cfm?URI=josaa-17-7-1319`.

22. Ellis, Troy R. and Jason D. Schmidt. "Hybrid Wavefront Sensor for Strong Turbulence". *Frontiers in Optics*, FMF2. Optical Society of America, 2008. URL `http://www.opticsinfobase.org/abstract.cfm?URI=URI=FiO-2008-FMF2`.

23. Flatté, Stanley M., Charles Bracher, and Guang-Yu Wang. "Probability-density functions of irradiance for waves in atmospheric turbulence calculated by numerical simulation". *J. Opt. Soc. Am. A*, 11(7):2080–2092, 1994. URL `http://josaa.osa.org/abstract.cfm?URI=josaa-11-7-2080`.

24. Flatté, Stanley M. and James S. Gerber. "Irradiance-variance behavior by numerical simulation for plane-wave and spherical-wave optical propagation through strong turbulence". *J. Opt. Soc. Am. A*, 17(6):1092–1097, 2000. URL http://josaa.osa.org/abstract.cfm?URI=josaa-17-6-1092.

25. Flatté, Stanley M., Guang-Yu Wang, and Jan Martin. "Irradiance variance of optical waves through atmospheric turbulence by numerical simulation and comparison with experiment". *J. Opt. Soc. Am. A*, 10(11):2363–2370, 1993. URL http://josaa.osa.org/abstract.cfm?URI=josaa-10-11-2363.

26. Freischlad, Klaus R. and Chris L. Koliopoulos. "Modal estimation of a wave front from difference measurements using the discrete Fourier transform". *J. Opt. Soc. Am. A*, 3(11):1852–1861, 1986. URL http://josaa.osa.org/abstract.cfm?URI=josaa-3-11-1852.

27. Fried, David L. "Optical Resolution through a Randomly Inhomogeneous Medium for Very Long and Very Short Exposures". *J. Opt. Soc. Am.*, 56(10):1372–1379, October 1966.

28. Fried, David L. "Least-square fitting a wave-front distortion estimate to an array of phase-difference measurements". *J. Opt. Soc. Am.*, 67(3):370–375, March 1977.

29. Fried, David L. "Branch point problem in adaptive optics". *J. Opt. Soc. Am. A*, 15(10):2759–2768, 1998. URL http://josaa.osa.org/abstract.cfm?URI=josaa-15-10-2759.

30. Fried, David L. "Adaptive optics wave function reconstruction and phase unwrapping when branch points are present". *Opt. Comm*, 200:43–72, 2001.

31. Fried, David L. and Jeffrey L. Vaughn. "Branch cuts in the phase function". *Appl. Opt.*, 31(15):2865–2882, 1992. URL http://ao.osa.org/abstract.cfm?URI=ao-31-15-2865.

32. Fusco, T., S. Thomas, M. Nicolle, A. Tokovinin, V. Michau, and G. Rousset. "Optimization of center of gravity algorithms in a Shack-Hartmann sensor". Brent L. Ellerbroek and Domenico Bonaccini Calia (editors), *Advances in Adaptive Optics II*, volume 6272 of *Proc. of SPIE*. SPIE, 2006.

33. Ghiglia, Dennis C. and Mark D. Pritt. *Two-Dimensional Phase Unwrapping: Theory, Algorithms, and Software*. John Wiley & Sons, 1998.

34. Goodman, Joseph W. *Statistical Optics*. John Wiley & Sons, Inc., New York, 2000.

35. Goodman, Joseph W. *Introduction to Fourier Optics*. Roberts & Company, Englewood, CO, third edition, 2005.

36. Hardy, John W. *Adaptive Optics for Astronomical Telescopes*. Oxford University Press, New York, 1998.

37. Hayt, William H. Jr. and John A. Buck. *Engineering Electromagnetics*. McGraw Hill, sixth edition, 2001.

38. Hecht, Eugene. *Optics*. Addison Wesley, New York, fourth edition, 2002.

39. Hill, Reginald J. and Rod G. Frehlich. "Probability distribution of irradiance for the onset of strong scintillation". *J. Opt. Soc. Am. A*, 14(7):1530–1540, 1997. URL http://josaa.osa.org/abstract.cfm?URI=josaa-14-7-1530.

40. Hudgin, Richard H. "Wave-front reconstruction for compensated imaging". *J. Opt. Soc. Am.*, 67(3):375–378, 1977. URL http://www.opticsinfobase.org/abstract.cfm?URI=josa-67-3-375.

41. Irwan, Roy and Richard. G. Lane. "Analysis of optimal centroid estimation applied to Shack-Hartmann sensing". *Appl. Opt.*, 38(32):6737–6743, 1999. URL http://ao.osa.org/abstract.cfm?URI=ao-38-32-6737.

42. Klein, Laura M. and Troy A. Rhoadarmer. "Closed-loop control techniques for an adaptive-optical system with an interferometric wavefront sensor". Michael K. Giles, John D. Gonglewski, and Richard A. Carreras (editors), *Advanced Wavefront Control: Methods, Devices, and Applications IV*, volume 6306. 2006.

43. Krane, Kenneth S. *Modern Physics*. John Wiley & Sons, Inc., 1996.

44. M. Servin, J.A. Quiroga J.F. Mosiño, J.C. Estrada and M. Cywiak. "Noise in phase shifting interferometry". *Opt. Exp.*, 17(11):8789–8794, May 2009.

45. Malacara, Daniel. *Optical Shop Testing*. John Wiley and Sons, New York, third edition, 2007.

46. Martin, J. M. and Stanley M. Flatté. "Simulation of point-source scintillation through three-dimensional random media". *J. Opt. Soc. Am. A*, 7(5):838–847, 1990. URL http://josaa.osa.org/abstract.cfm?URI=josaa-7-5-838.

47. MathWorks. "MATLAB®'s unwrap function". MATLAB® Student Version 7.1, June 2004.

48. Maxwell, James Clerk. *A Treatise on Electricity and Magnetism*. Oxford University Press, London, third edition, 1892. First Edition 1873, Second Edition 1881,Third Edition 1892; Reprinted 1904. Reprinted photographically in 1937, 1946 by Lowe & Brydone, Printers, LTD., London from sheets of the third edition.

49. Noll, R.J. "Zernike polynomials and atmospheric turbulence". *J. Opt. Soc. Am.*, 66:207–211, 1976.

50. Noll, R.J. "Phase estimates from slope-type wave-front sensors". *J. Opt. Soc. Am.*, 68:139–140, 1977.

51. Paterson, C. and J. C. Dainty. "Hybrid curvature and gradient wave-front sensor". *Opt. Lett.*, 25(23):1687–1689, 2000. URL http://ol.osa.org/abstract.cfm?URI=ol-25-23-1687.

52. Pellizzari, C. and J.D. Schmidt. "Phase unwrapping in the presence of strong turbulence". 1 –10. mar. 2010. ISSN 1095-323X.

53. Pellizzari, Casey J. *Phase Unwrapping in the Presence of Strong Turbulence.* Master's thesis, Air Force Institute of Technology, March 2010.

54. Phillips, James D. and Stephen C. Cain. "Joint maximum likelihood estimator for pupil and image plane data". *Opt. Eng.*, 47(2):026002, 2008. URL `http://link.aip.org/link/?JOE/47/026002/1`.

55. Poor, H. Vincent. *An Introduction to Signal Detection and Estimation.* Springer, second edition, 1994.

56. Poyneer, Lisa A. "Scene-Based Shack-Hartmann Wave-Front Sensing: Analysis and Simulation". *Appl. Opt.*, 42(29):5807–5815, 2003. URL `http://ao.osa.org/abstract.cfm?URI=ao-42-29-5807`.

57. Poyneer, Lisa A., Donald T. Gavel, and James M. Brase. "Fast wavefront reconstruction in large adaptive optics systems with use of the Fourier transform". *J. Opt. Soc. Am. A*, 19(10):2100–2111, 2002. URL `http://josaa.osa.org/abstract.cfm?URI=josaa-19-10-2100`.

58. Poyneer, Lisa A., David W. Palmer, Kai N. LaFortune, and Brian Bauman. "Experimental results for correlation-based wavefront sensing". Mark T. Gruneisen, John D. Gonglewski, and Michael K. Giles (editors), *Advanced Wavefront Control: Methods, Devices, and Applications III*, volume 5894, 58940N. SPIE, 2005. URL `http://link.aip.org/link/?PSI/5894/58940N/1`.

59. Primmerman, Charles A., Thomas R. Price, Ronald A. Humphreys, Byron G. Zollars, Herbert T. Barclay, and Jan Herrmann. "Atmospheric-compensation experiments in strong-scintillation conditions". *Appl. Opt.*, 34(12):2081–2088, 1995. URL `http://ao.osa.org/abstract.cfm?URI=ao-34-12-2081`.

60. Pritt, M.D. "Congruence in least-squares phase unwrapping". *International Geoscience and Remote Sensing Symposium*, 2:875–877, 1997.

61. R.E.Wagner and W.J.Tomlinson. "Coupling efficiency of optics in single-mode fiber components". *Appl.Opt.*, 21:2671–2688, 1982.

62. Rhoadarmer, Troy A. "Wave front reconstruction using a second-order model for Shack-Hartmann wavefront sensor measurements". William E. Thompson and Paul H. Merritt (editors), *Laser Weapons Technology III*, volume 4724, 17–29. SPIE, 2002. URL `http://link.aip.org/link/?PSI/4724/17/1`.

63. Rhoadarmer, Troy A. "Development of a self-referencing interferometer wavefront sensor". John D. Gonglewski, Mark T. Gruneisen, and Michael K. Giles (editors), *Advanced Wavefront Control: Methods, Devices, and Applications II*, volume 5553, 112–126. SPIE, 2004. URL `http://link.aip.org/link/?PSI/5553/112/1`.

64. Rhoadarmer, Troy A. and Jeffrey D. Barchers. "Noise analysis for complex field estimation using a self-referencing interferometer wave front sensor". volume 4825, 215–227. SPIE, 2002. URL http://link.aip.org/link/?PSI/4825/215/1.

65. Robert, Clelia, Jean-Marc Conan, Vincent Michau, Thierry Fusco, and Nicolas Vedrenne. "Scintillation and phase anisoplanatism in Shack-Hartmann wavefront sensing". *J. Opt. Soc. Am. A*, 24(3):613–624, 2006.

66. Roddier, F. "Theoretical Aspects". F. Roddier (editor), *Adaptive Optics in Astronomy*, chapter 3. Cambridge University Press, 1999.

67. Roggemann, Michael C. and Timothy J. Schulz. "Algorithm to increase the largest aberration that can be reconstructed from Hartmann sensor measurements". *Appl. Opt.*, 37(20):4321–4329, 1998. URL http://ao.osa.org/abstract.cfm?URI=ao-37-20-4321.

68. Roggemann, Michael C., Timothy J. Schulz, Chee W. Ngai, and Jason T. Kraft. "Joint Processing of Hartmann Sensor and Conventional Image Measurements to Estimate Large Aberrations: Theory and Experimental Results". *Appl. Opt.*, 38(11):2249–2255, 1999. URL http://ao.osa.org/abstract.cfm?URI=ao-38-11-2249.

69. Ross, Sheldon. *A First Course in Probability*. Prentice Hall, Upper Saddle River, New Jersey, sixth edition, 2002. ISBN 0-13-033851-6.

70. Sallberg, Scott A., Byron M. Welsh, and Michael C. Roggemann. "Maximum *a posteriori* estimation of wave-front slopes using a Shack-Hartmann wave-front sensor". *J.Opt.Soc.Am. A*, 14(6):1347–1354, June 1997.

71. Sasiela, Richard J. *Electromagnetic Wave Propagation in Turbulence, Evaluation and Applications of Mellin Transforms*. MIT Lincoln Laboratory, Lexington, Massachusetts, second edition, 2006.

72. Schmidt, Jason D. *Numerical Simulation of Optical Wave Propagation with Examples in MATLAB*. SPIE Press, Bellingham, WA, 2010. ISBN 9780819483270. URL http://link.aip.org/link/doi/10.1117/3.866274.

73. Sergeyev, Aleksandr V., Piotr Piatrou, and Michael C. Roggemann. "Bootstrap beacon creation for overcoming the effects of beacon anisoplanatism in a laser beam projection system". *Appl. Opt.*, 47(13):2399–2413, 2008. URL http://ao.osa.org/abstract.cfm?URI=ao-47-13-2399.

74. Shack, R.V. and B.C. Platt. "Program of the 1971 Spring Meeting of the Optical Society of America". *J. Opt. Soc. Am.*, 61(5):648–648, 1971. URL http://www.opticsinfobase.org/abstract.cfm?URI=josa-61-5-648.

75. Shack, R.V. and B.C. Platt. "Coupling starlight into single-mode fiber optics". *Appl.Opt.*, 27:2334–2338, 1988.

76. Southwell, W. H. "Wave-front estimation from wave-front slope measurements". *J. Opt. Soc. Am.*, 70(8):998, 1980. URL http://www.opticsinfobase.org/abstract.cfm?URI=josa-70-8-998.

77. of Standards, National Institute. "International System of Units (SI)". National Institute of Standards and Technology, October 2000. URL http://physics.nist.gov/cuu/Units.

78. Thomas, S., S. Adkins, D. Gavel, T. Fusco, and V. Michau. "Study of optimal wavefront sensing with elongated laser guide stars". *Mon. Not. R. Astron. Soc.*, 387:173–187, 2008.

79. Thomas, S., T. Fusco, A. Tokovinin, M. Nicolle, , and G. R. V. Michau. "Comparison of centroid computation algorithms in a Shack-Hartmann sensor". *Mon. Not. R. Astron. Soc.*, 371:323–336, 2006.

80. Toyoshima, Morio, Hideki Takenaka, Yozo Shoji, Yoshihisa Takayama, Yoshisada Koyama, and Hiroo Kunimori. "Polarization measurements through space-to-ground atmospheric propagation paths by using a highly polarized laser source in space". *Opt. Express*, 17(25):22333–22340, 2009. URL http://www.opticsexpress.org/abstract.cfm?URI=oe-17-25-22333.

81. Tyler, Glenn A. "Reconstruction and assessment of the least-squares and slope discrepancy components of the phase". *J. Opt. Soc. Am. A*, 17(10):1828–1839, 2000.

82. Tyler, Glenn A. "Adaptive optics compensation for propagation through deep turbulence: initial investigation of gradient descent tomography". *J. Opt. Soc. Am. A*, 23(8):1914–1923, 2006. URL http://josaa.osa.org/abstract.cfm?URI=josaa-23-8-1914.

83. Tyler, Glenn A. and David L. Fried. "Image-position error associated with a quadrant detector". *J. Opt. Soc. Am.*, 72(6):804–808, June 1932.

84. Van Trees, Harry L. *Detection, Estimation, and Modulation Theory Part I*. John Wiley and Sons, Inc., 1968.

85. Vedrenne, Nicolas, Vincent Michau, Clelia Robert, and Jean-Marc Conan. "Shack-Hartmann wavefront estimation with extended sources: anisoplanatism influence". *J. Opt. Soc. Am. A*, 24(9):2980–2993, 2007.

86. Venema, Todd. M. and Jason D. Schmidt. "Optical phase unwrapping in the presence of Branch Points". *Opt. Express*, 16(10), May 2008.

87. Vorontsov, Mikhail A., Valeriy V. Kolosov, and Ernst Polnau. "Target-in-the-loop wavefront sensing and control with a Collett-Wolf beacon: speckle-average phase conjugation". *Appl. Opt.*, 48(1):A13–A29, 2009. URL http://ao.osa.org/abstract.cfm?URI=ao-48-1-A13.

88. Wallner, Edward P. "Optimal wave-front correction using slope measurements". *J. Opt. Soc. Am.*, 73(12):1771–1776, 1983. URL `http://www.opticsinfobase.org/abstract.cfm?URI=josa-73-12-1771`.

89. Welsh, Byron M., Brent L. Ellerbroek, Michale C. Roggemann, and Timothy L. Pennington. "Fundamental performance comparison of a Hartmann and a shearing interferometer wave-front sensor". *Appl. Opt.*, 34(21):4186–4195, July 1995.

90. Welsh, Byron M. and Chester S. Gardner. "Performance analysis of adaptive-optics systems using laser guide stars and slope sensors". *J. Opt. Soc. Am. A*, 6(12):1913–1923, 1989. URL `http://josaa.osa.org/abstract.cfm?URI=josaa-6-12-1913`.

91. Winick, Kim A. "Cramér-Rao lower bounds on the performance of charge-coupled-device optical position estimators". *J. Opt. Soc. Am. A*, 3(11):1809–1815, 1986. URL `http://josaa.osa.org/abstract.cfm?URI=josaa-3-11-1809`.

92. Xiao, Xifeng and David Voelz. "Wave optics simulation approach for partial spatially coherent beams". *Opt. Express*, 14(16):6986–6992, 2006. URL `http://www.opticsexpress.org/abstract.cfm?URI=oe-14-16-6986`.

93. Yariv, Amnon and Pochi Yeh. *Optical Waves in Crystals: Propagation and Control of Laser Radiation*. John Wiley & Sons, Inc., 2003.

REPORT DOCUMENTATION PAGE

Form Approved
OMB No. 074-0188

1. REPORT DATE (DD-MM-YYYY) 24-03-2011	2. REPORT TYPE Doctoral Dissertation	3. DATES COVERED (From – To) Jun 2007 - Mar 2011

4. TITLE AND SUBTITLE		5a. CONTRACT NUMBER
Shack-Hartmann and Interferometric Hybrid Wavefront Sensor		5b. GRANT NUMBER F1ATA08350J002
		5c. PROGRAM ELEMENT NUMBER

6. AUTHOR(S)	5d. PROJECT NUMBER ENGJON229
Ellis, Troy, R. Captain, USAF	5e. TASK NUMBER
	5f. WORK UNIT NUMBER

7. PERFORMING ORGANIZATION NAMES(S) AND ADDRESS(S) Air Force Institute of Technology Graduate School of Engineering and Management (AFIT/EN) 2950 Hobson Way WPAFB OH 45433-7765	8. PERFORMING ORGANIZATION REPORT NUMBER AFIT/DEO/ENG/11-01

9. SPONSORING/MONITORING AGENCY NAME(S) AND ADDRESS(ES) Air Force Office of Scientific Research Kent Miller 3875 Randolph St., Ste. 3112 Arlington, VA 22203 (703) 696-8573, kent.miller@afosr.af.mil	10. SPONSOR/MONITOR'S ACRONYM(S) AFOSR/NE
	11. SPONSOR/MONITOR'S REPORT NUMBER(S)

12. DISTRIBUTION/AVAILABILITY STATEMENT APPROVED FOR PUBLIC RELEASE; DISTRIBUTION UNLIMITED. THIS MATERIAL IS DECLARED A WORK OF THE U.S. GOVERNMENT AND IS NOT SUBJECT TO COPYRIGHT PROTECTION IN THE UNITED STATES.

13. SUPPLEMENTARY NOTES

14. ABSTRACT

This document reports results of wave-optics simulations used to test the performance of a hybrid wavefront sensor designed to combine the self-referencing interferometer and Shack-Hartmann wavefront sensors in an optimal way. Optimal hybrid-wavefront sensor design required a thorough analysis of the noise characteristics of each wavefront sensor to produce noise models that assist in the design of an optimal phase-estimation algorithm. Feasible architectures and algorithms for combining wavefront sensors were chosen, and the noise models of the individual wavefront sensors were combined to form a model for the noise-induced error of the resulting hybrid sensor. The hybrid wavefront sensor and phase-estimation algorithm developed through this work showed improvement over a comparable stand-alone self-referencing interferometer and Shack-Hartmann wavefront sensor in open-loop wave-optics simulations.

15. SUBJECT TERMS

wavefront sensor, self-referencing interferometer, Shack-Hartmann sensor, atmospheric turbulence, directed-energy beam control, adaptive optics, maximum-likelihood estimation

16. SECURITY CLASSIFICATION OF:			17. LIMITATION OF ABSTRACT	18. NUMBER OF PAGES	19a. NAME OF RESPONSIBLE PERSON Jason D. Schmidt, Maj, USAF (ENG)
REPORT U	ABSTRACT U	c. THIS PAGE U	UU	194	19b. TELEPHONE NUMBER (Include area code) COM: (937) 255-3636, DSN: 785-3636, x7224 Jason.Schmidt@afit.edu

Standard Form 298 (Rev. 8-98)
Prescribed by ANSI Std. Z39-18

Lightning Source UK Ltd.
Milton Keynes UK
UKHW031256220222
399070UK00006B/1063

9 781288 327423